MIGRATION OF BIRDS

MIGRATION
of BIRDS

By **FREDERICK C. LINCOLN**
Biologist

Fish and Wildlife Service, U.S. Department of the Interior

Illustrated by **BOB HINES**

Doubleday & Company, Inc., Garden City, New York, 1952

Library of Congress
Catalogue Card Number: 52-5234

The source of this material is a publication of the Fish and
Wildlife Service of the United States Department of the Interior.

PRINTED IN THE UNITED STATES OF AMERICA

Contents

MIGRATION OF BIRDS

MIGRATION
of BIRDS

When the birds that have nested in our dooryards and those that have frequented the neighboring woods, hills, and marshes leave us in the fall, the question naturally comes to mind: Where do they go? This, however, is only one small part of the question as we also wonder: Will the same ones return next spring to their former haunts? What dangers will they face on their round-trip flight and while in their winter homes? These and other questions on the migratory habits of most species of Northern Hemisphere birds puzzle all who are interested in them, whether it be the farmer who profits by their tireless warfare against the weed and insect pests of his crops, the bird student who enjoys an abundance and variety of feathered inhabitants about him, or the hunter who wants a continuation from year to year of the sport of wildfowling. Lack of information on the subject may mean the loss of an important resource by unconsciously letting it slip from us, as ignorance might be responsible for inadequate legal protection for such species as might urgently need it. More general knowledge on the subject will aid in the perpetuation of the various migrants, the seasonal habitats of some of which are in grave danger from man's utilization, sometimes unwisely, of the marsh, water and other areas that were formerly homes for birds.

The migrations of birds were probably among the first natural phenomena to attract the attention and intrigue the imagination of man. Recorded observations on the subject date back nearly 3,000 years, to the times of Hesiod, Homer, Herodotus, Aristotle, and others. In the Bible there are several references to the periodic movements of birds, as in the Book of Job (39:26), where the inquiry is made: "Doth the hawk fly by Thy wisdom and stretch her wings toward the south?" Jeremiah (8:7), wrote: "The stork in the heavens knoweth her appointed time; and the turtle [dove], and the crane, and the swallow, observe the time of their coming." And the flight of quail that saved the Israelites from starvation in their wanderings in the wilderness of Sinai is now recognized as a vast movement of migratory quail between their breeding grounds and their winter home in Africa.

Throughout the ages the return flights of migratory birds have been important as a source of food after a lean winter and as the harbinger of a change in season. The arrival of certain species has been heralded with appropriate ceremonies in many lands, and among the Eskimos and other tribes the phenomenon to this day is the accepted sign of the imminence of spring and of warmer weather. The pioneer fur traders in Alaska and Canada offered rewards to the Indian or Eskimo who saw the first goose of the spring, and all joined in jubilant welcome to the newcomer.

As the North American Continent became more thickly settled, the large flocks of ducks and geese that always had been hunted for food became objects of the enthusiastic attention of an increasing army of sportsmen. Most of the nongame species were found to be valuable also as allies of the farmer in his never-ending warfare against weed and insect pests. The need for laws protecting the valuable game and nongame birds and for regulating the hunting of the diminishing game species followed as a natural course. In the management of this wildlife resource it has become obvious that continuous studies must be made of the food habits of the various species, their environmental needs, and their travels. Hence bird investigations are made by the Fish and Wildlife Service, the bureau charged by Congress under the Migratory Bird Treaty Act with the duty of protecting those species that in their yearly journeys pass back and forth between the United States and Canada, and between the United States and Mexico.

For more than half a century the Fish and Wildlife Service and its predecessor, the Biological Survey, have been collecting data on the interesting and important phenomenon of the migration of North American birds. The field men of the Service have gathered information concerning the distribution and seasonal movements of the different species in many extended areas, from the Arctic coast south to the pampas of Argentina. Supplementing these investigations is the work of hundreds of volunteer ornithologists and bird students throughout the United States and Canada, who each year, spring and fall, forward to the Service reports on the migrations as observed in their respective localities. Added to the mass of data thus assembled is a rapidly growing recovery file of marked individuals. These data, together with other carded records gleaned by the Fish and Wildlife Service from a vast literature, constitute a series of files that now contain well over 3,000,000 entries, easily the greatest existing accumulation of information pertaining to the distribution and movements of North American birds. Not only do the facts thus assembled form the basis of regulatory action for the protection of the birds, but they also make it possible to publish scientific accounts of the ranges and migrations of the different species. They furnish the basis of this bulletin.

The several important bird-protective measures adopted by State and Federal Governments, particularly those having as their objectives the conservation of the migratory song, insectivorous, and game species, can be effective only if they have intelligent public support. To increase such support, information must be more generally available on that little understood but universally fascinating subject of bird migration. A brief presentation of facts on the migratory habits of the birds scientifically gathered by the Fish and Wildlife Service over many years, will be helpful to bird-study classes, to conservation organizations, and to farmers and others individually interested in the welfare of the birds.

In addition to his original investigations in the field and in the files of the Fish and Wildlife Service, the author has made free use of the writings of many other students of the subject. To all of these grateful acknowledgment is made.

The Mystery of Migration

Of observers whose writings are extant, Aristotle, naturalist and philosopher of ancient Greece, was one of the first to discuss the subject of bird migration. He noted that cranes traveled from the steppes of Scythia to the marshes at the headwaters of the Nile, and that pelicans, geese, swans, rails, doves, and many other birds likewise passed to warmer regions to spend the winter. In the earliest years of the Christian era, the elder Pliny, Roman naturalist, in his Historia Naturalis, repeated much of what Aristotle had said on migration and added comments of his own concerning the movements of the European blackbird, the starling, and the thrushes.

In spite of the keen perception shown in some of his statements Aristotle also must be credited with the origin of some superstitious beliefs that persisted for several centuries. One of these, that of hibernation, became so firmly rooted that Dr. Elliott Coues (1878),[1] one of America's greatest ornithologists, listed the titles of no less than 182 papers dealing with the hibernation of swallows. The hibernation theory accounted for the autumnal disappearance of certain species of birds by having them pass into a torpid state and so remain during the cold season, hidden in hollow trees, caves, or in the mud of marshes. Aristotle ascribed hibernation not only to swallows, but also to storks, kites, doves, and others. Some early naturalists wrote fantastic accounts of the flocks of swallows that allegedly were seen congregating in the marshes until their accumulated weight bent into the water the reeds on which they clung and thus submerged the birds. It was even recorded that when fishermen in northern waters drew up their nets they sometimes had a mixed "catch" of fish and hibernating swallows. Clarke (1912) quotes Olaus Magnus, Archbishop of Upsala, who in 1555 published a work entitled "Historia de Gentibus Septentrionalis et Natura," wherein he observed that if swallows so caught were taken into a warm room they would soon begin to fly about but would live only a short time.

The hibernation theory survived for more than 2,000 years and, until the winter home of the chimney swift was discovered in 1944 through the recovery of banded individuals, it was occasionally repeated by credulous persons to account for the sudden disappearance of the immense flocks that each autumn gather in southern Georgia and north-

---

[1] Publications referred to parenthetically by date are listed in the Bibliography, p. 94.

ern Florida. Although the winter range is still unknown in fullest detail, Lincoln (1944b) has shown that some of these birds spend the winter season in northeastern Peru.

Although the idea that hibernation is a regular feature of the life cycle of birds is no longer accepted for any species, recognition must be accorded the observations of Edmund C. Jaeger of Riverside College, Riverside, Calif. (1949). Earlier (1948), he had given a brief account of the behavior of a poorwill found during the winter of 1946–47 in the Chukawalla Mountains of the Colorado Desert, Calif., and which was in a state of profound torpidity.

What was presumably the same individual was found in the same rock niche in a comatose condition on November 26, 1947. Beginning on December 30, 1947, rectal temperatures were taken every 2 weeks, the last on February 14, 1948. The temperature dropped from 67.6° on the first date to 64.4° on January 18 and February 1, recovering to 65.8° on the late date of record. The weight decreased from 45.61 grams on January 4 to 44.56 grams on February 14. An attempt to detect heart beat by the use of a medical stethoscope was negative. No movement of the chest walls could be detected and no moisture could be collected on a cold mirror placed in front of the nostrils. Strong light aimed directly into the pupil resulted in no response, not even an attempt to close the eyelid. No waste matter was passed during the entire period of observation and all evidence indicated that the bird was in an exceedingly low state of metabolism.

This bird was banded on January 5, 1948, with a Service band and was back in the same rock niche on November 24, 1948, certainly the second and probably the third season of return to this exact point. It was there on December 5, 1948, but 2 weeks later it had disappeared, probably the victim of some predator or an inquisitive human. Professor Jaeger reports that the Hopi Indians call the poorwill "Holchko," the sleeping one.

Aristotle also was the originator of the theory of transmutation, basing it upon the fact that frequently one species will arrive from the north just as another species departs for more southerly latitudes. From this he reasoned that although it was commonly believed that such birds were of two different species, there really was only one, and that this one assumed the different plumages to correspond with the summer and winter seasons.

Probably the most remarkable theory that has been advanced to account for migration is contained in a pamphlet mentioned by Clarke (1912: v. 1, 9–11) as published in 1703 under the title: "An Essay Toward the Probable Solution of this Question: Whence come the Stork and the Turtle, the Crane, and the Swallow, when they Know and Observe the Appointed Time of their Coming." It was written "By a Person of Learning and Piety," whose "probable solution" was that migratory birds flew to the moon and there spent the winter.

Some peoples, who easily accepted the migratory travels of the larger birds, were unable to understand how the smaller species, some of them notoriously poor fliers, could make similar journeys. They accordingly conceived the idea that the larger species, as the storks and cranes, carried their smaller companions as living freight. In some of the Mediterranean countries, it is still believed that these broad-pinioned birds serve as aerial transports for the hosts of small birds that congregate upon the shores awaiting opportunity for this kind of passage to their winter homes in Africa. Similar beliefs have been found among some tribes of North American Indians.

Advantages of Migration

Before presenting some of the present theories concerning the origin of bird migration, it seems well to consider briefly the ends that are served by this annual round trip between breeding grounds and winter quarters. It is apparent that the migratory habit enables a species to enjoy the summers of northern latitudes while avoiding the severity of the winters. In other words, migration makes it possible for some species to inhabit two different areas during the seasons when each presents favorable conditions. In the performance of its reproductive duties, every pair of birds requires a certain amount of territory, the extent of which varies greatly in different species. Generally, however, this territory must be large enough to provide adequate food, not only for the parent birds, but also for the lusty appetites that come into being with the hatching of the eggs. Thus, if all birds were to remain constantly either in tropical or in temperate regions, there would be intolerable overcrowding during the breeding season. By the spring withdrawal to regions uninhabitable earlier in the year, the migrants are assured of adequate space and ample food upon their arrival in the winter-freed North, and it may be assumed that the nonmigratory species that are resident in the South are also benefited by the departure of the migrants.

Nevertheless, it cannot be said that the winter or summer area of every species is entirely unsuited to its requirements at other seasons, for some individuals pass the winter season in areas that are frequented only in summer by other individuals of their species. Such species have extensive breeding ranges, presenting wide climatic variations, so that some individuals may actually be resident in a region where others of their kind are present only in winter.

The tendency of some birds to move southward at the approach of winter is not always due to the seasonal low temperatures, since experiments have demonstrated that many of our summer insect feeders, when confined in outdoor aviaries, comfortably withstand temperatures far below zero. The main consideration is the depletion of the food supply, caused either by the disappearance or the hibernation of insects, or by the mantle of snow or ice that prevents access to the seeds and other forms of food found on or close to the ground or submerged in water. Possibly also the shortened hours of daylight materially restrict the ability of the birds to obtain sufficient food at a time when the cold requires an increased supply to maintain body heat. It is noteworthy that some of our smaller birds, such as the chickadees, have no fear of Arctic weather, as their food supplies are entirely arboreal and so are always available. Also, when there is a good supply of food in the form of pine and spruce seeds, nuthatches and crossbills will remain through the winter in Canadian woods. When these birds appear abundantly in winter at points in southern latitudes, it may be concluded that there is a shortage of their food in the North.

The Origin of Migration

Migration has long since become a definite hereditary habit that recurs in annual cycles, probably because of physiological stimulus associated with the reproductive period. Its origin is locked in the ages of geologic time, but by study of the history of how birds came to occupy their present ranges, information becomes available from which reasonable theories may be developed and explored. The two that are most commonly accepted are diametrically opposed to each other.

Northern ancestral home theory

According to one of these hypotheses, in earlier ages nonmigratory birds swarmed over the entire Northern Hemisphere. At that time the conditions of food and habitat were such as to permit them to remain in their haunts throughout the year, that is, the entire northern area then afforded the two important avian requirements—suitable breeding conditions, and year-long food supply. This is the condition today in the Tropics, and it is noteworthy that, as a rule, tropical birds do not perform migrations. Gradually, however, in the Northern Hemisphere the glacial ice fields advanced southward, forcing the birds before them, until finally all bird life was concentrated in southern latitudes. As the ages passed the ice cap gradually retreated, and each spring the birds whose ancestral home had been in the North endeavored to return, only to be driven south again at the approach of winter. As the size of the ice-covered area diminished the journeys made became ever longer until eventually the climatic conditions of the present age became established and with them the habit of migration.

Thus, this theory supposes that today migratory birds follow the path of a great racial movement that took place in a distant past and was associated with the advances and recessions of the ice. The actions of the birds themselves lend some support to this theory, as every bird student has noted the feverish impatience with which certain species push northward in spring, sometimes advancing so rapidly upon the heels of winter that they perish in great numbers when overtaken by late storms. It is probable that at this season the reproductive impulse is a determining factor in driving the birds to their northern breeding grounds.

Southern ancestral home theory

The opposing theory is simpler in some respects and supposes that the ancestral home of all birds was in the Tropics and that, as all bird life tends to overpopulation, there was a constant effort to seek breeding grounds where the competition would be less keen. Species that strove for more northern latitudes were kept in check by the ice and were forced to return southward with the recurrence of winter conditions. Gradually, as the ice retreated, vast areas of virgin country became successively suitable for summer occupancy, but the winter habitat remained the home to which the birds returned after the nest-

8

ing season. It is a fact that some species spend very little time on their breeding grounds; the orchard oriole, for example, spends only 2½ months in its summer home, arriving in southern Pennsylvania about the first week in May and leaving by the middle of July.

Both of these theories assume that migration is an ingrained habit, but both have been criticized on biological and geological grounds, so neither should be accepted without qualification as definitely account ing for the origin of bird migration. It is apparent, however, that whether the ancestral home of any species was at the northern or southern limits of its present range, or even in some intermediate region, the search for favorable conditions under which to breed in summer and to feed in winter has been the principal factor underlying the origin of migration.

Theory of photoperiodism

A modern view based on studies of living behavior, suggests also that there is good reason for believing that migration is an annually induced movement. If such be true then the theory of photoperiodism as propounded by some recent investigators should receive some consideration.

This theory holds as its major premise that quantity of light and length of day are the stimulating causes of migration. Its proponents urge that migration is a phenomenon far too regular to be created anew each season merely under stress of circumstances, such as need for food; and that it begins before the necessity for a change in latitude becomes at all pressing. Swallows, nighthawks, shore birds, and others may start their southward movement while the summer food supply in the North is at peak abundance; while robins, bluebirds, and others may leave an abundant food in the South in spring and press toward northern points when food supplies there are almost entirely lacking and when severe cold and storms are likely to cause their wholesale destruction. The regularity of arrival and departure is one of the most impressive features of migration, and since birds travel in almost strict accordance with the calendar, the proponents of the theory ask: "What phenomenon to which we may attribute the stimulating impulse occurs with such precise regularity as the constantly increasing amount of light in spring?"

Experimental work has abundantly demonstrated the effect of increased light upon the growth, flowering, and fruiting of plants.

Similarly, experiments with the common junco or snowbird reported by Rowan (1931: 121), resulted in increased development of the sexual organs by the end of December, although the birds were confined in outdoor aviaries in Canada, and had been exposed to temperatures as low as $-44°$ F. From the first of November until early in January, the juncos were subjected to ever-increasing light, supplied in the aviaries by electric bulbs. As regards illumination, they were thus artificially provided with conditions approximating those of spring. At the close of this period, it was found that the sexual organs of the birds had attained the maximum development normally associated with spring. With gradual reduction of the lighting over a period of little more than 1 month, the organs returned to their normal winter condition.

After a consideration of all evidence, including the fact that no ultra-violet rays were used, it was concluded that the explanation lay in the increased exercise taken during the periods of increased light. A simple test whereby certain birds were forced by mechanical means to take more exercise, the light being so reduced that there was merely sufficient glow for them to see the advancing mechanism that forced them into movement, showed that the rate of development of the sexual organs exactly paralleled that in the birds that were exposed to extended periods of illumination in the outdoor aviaries. Other features in this experiment—such as the behavior of the birds themselves—also indicated that more activity due to increased light is the governing cause of the spring development of the sexual organs. If this development be accepted as a controlling cause of migration, then this experiment must be recognized as of great importance.

Upon closer analysis, however, it is found that this theory, like those before discussed, is open to serious objections. First, some of our summer residents that migrate south for the winter do not stop in equatorial regions, where they might find the periods of day and night about equally divided, but push on beyond, some penetrating as far south as Patagonia. Also it might be asked: "If the lengthening day is the stimulating factor, why should our summer birds wintering in the Tropics ever start northward, as in their winter quarters the variation in the length of day from winter to summer is imperceptible?" Like all the other theories advanced, this also, as at present understood, is subject to unanswered criticism.

Theory of continental drift

The theory of continental drift postulates an original northern land mass, called Laurasia, and a southern one, called Gondwana. According to this concept, each eventually broke into several segments which eventually became the present continents. It is further assumed that occasionally Laurasia and Gondwana drifted close to one another or were at times in actual contact. On the basis of this geological theory, Wolfson (1940) has attempted to explain the migrations of some species of birds from one hemisphere to the other, as, for example, the Greenland wheatear, Arctic tern, and several shore birds (turnstone, sanderling, knot, golden plover, and others). Acceptance of this hypothesis requires abandonment of the belief that the development of migration was the result of useful ends that were served thereby, and in its place, to give approval to the idea that migration was merely "the natural consequence of an inherent behavior pattern responding to the drifting of continental masses."

It is a strange fact that although almost all professional paleontologists are agreed that existing data oppose the theory of continental drift, those who support it contend that their case is strengthened by these same data. If, in the geologic history of the earth, there was any such thing as continental drift, it appears from the evidence available that it was before the Cretaceous period, estimated to have been about 70,000,000 years ago. Birds had then evolved but those known from fossil remains were of extremely primitive types such as Hesperornis and Ichthyornis. There is no evidence of the existence in that period of any birds that were even closely related to any of those now living. Accordingly, it is difficult to believe that the migratory patterns of existing species have been determined by events that, if they did take place, were at least 70,000,000 or more years ago.

When Birds Migrate

It is known that at any given point many species leave in the fall and return in the spring. Since banding has had such wide application as a method of study, it is known also that in some species one of the parent birds (rarely both) frequently returns and nests in the tree, bush, or box that held its nest in the previous season. One ordinarily thinks of the world of birds as quiescent during two periods each year,

11

at nesting time, and in winter. For individuals this is obviously the case, but when the entire avifauna of the continent is considered it is found that there are at almost all periods some latitudinal movements.

Movements of species and groups

Some species begin their fall migrations early in July and in some parts of the country distinct southward movements can be detected from then until the beginning or middle of winter. For example, many shore birds start south in the early part of July, while the goshawks, snowy owls, redpolls, Bohemian waxwings, and many others do not leave the North until forced to do so by the advent of severe winter weather, or by lack of the customary food. Thus an observer in the northern part of the United States may record an almost unbroken southward procession of birds from midsummer to winter, and note some of the returning migrants as early as the middle of February. While on their way north, purple martins have been known to arrive in Florida late in January and, among late arrivals, the northern movement may continue into the first week of June. In some species the migration is so prolonged that the first arrivals in the southern part of the breeding range will have performed their parental duties while others of that species are still on their way north.

A study of these facts indicates that sometimes there exists a very definite relationship between what we may term northern and southern groups of individuals of the same species. A supposition is that for a species with an extensive latitudinal breeding range, and which has a normal migration, those individuals that nest farthest south migrate first and proceed to the southern part of the winter range; those that occupy the central parts of the breeding range migrate next and travel to regions in the winter range north of those occupied by the first group; and finally the individuals breeding farthest north are the last to start their autumn migration and they remain farthest north during the winter. In other words, this theory supposes that the southward movement of the species is such that the different groups maintain their relative latitudinal position with each other. The black and white warbler furnishes an example. The breeding range of this bird extends west and northwest from northern Georgia and South Carolina to New Brunswick, extending also in a western and northwestern direction as far as Great Bear Lake in northwestern Canada (fig. 1). It

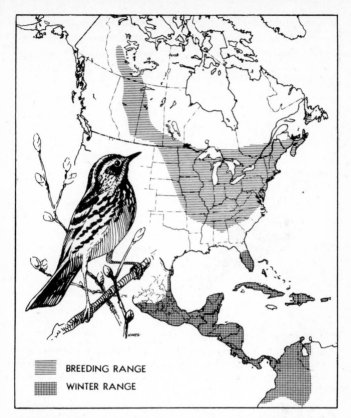

BREEDING RANGE
WINTER RANGE

Figure 1.—Summer and winter homes of the black and white warbler,
a very slow migrant as the birds nesting in the northern part of the
country take 50 days to cross the breeding range. The speed of
migration is shown in figure 2. (See p. 14.)

spends the winter in southern Florida, the West Indies, central Mexico,
Central America, and northwestern South America. In the southern
part of its breeding range it is nesting in April, but those that summer
in New Brunswick do not reach their nesting grounds before the
middle of May. Therefore, about 50 days are required for these northbound birds to cross the breeding range, and if 60 days be allowed for
nest building, egg laying, incubation, care of young, and molt, they
would not be ready to start southward before the middle of July

Figure 2.—Isochronal migration lines of the black and white warbler, showing a very slow and uniform migration. These birds apparently advance only about 20 miles a day in crossing the United States. (See p. 13.)

(fig. 2.). Then another 50-day trip south, and the earliest migrants from the northern areas would reach the Gulf Coast in September. But both adults and young have been observed at Key West, Fla., by the middle of July, and on the northern coast of South America by August 21. Since the birds at Key West were fully 500 miles south of the breeding range, it is evident that they must have come from the southern part of the nesting area.

Many similar cases might be mentioned, such as the black-throated blue warblers, which are still observed in the mountains of Haiti in the middle of May, when others of this species are en route through North Carolina to breeding territory in New England or have even reached that region. Redstarts and yellow warblers, evidently the more southern breeders, are seen returning southward on the northern coast of South America just about the time that the earliest of those breeding in the North reach Florida on their way to winter quarters.

Nocturnal and diurnal migration

When one recalls that most birds appear to be more or less helpless in the dark, it seems remarkable that many should select the night hours for extended travel. Among those that do, however, are the great hosts of shore birds, rails, flycatchers, orioles, most of the great family of sparrows, the warblers, vireos, and thrushes, and in fact, the majority of small birds. That it is common to find woods and fields on one day almost barren of bird life, and on the following day filled with sparrows, warblers, and thrushes, would indicate the arrival of migrants during the night. Sportsmen sitting in their "blinds" frequently observe the passage of flocks of ducks and geese, but great numbers of these birds also pass through at night, the clarion call of the Canada goose, or the conversational gabbling of a flock of ducks being common night sounds in spring and fall in many parts of the country. The sibilant, nocturnal calls of the upland plover or Bartramian sandpiper and of other shore birds during their spring and fall flights form vivid memories in the minds of many students of migration. Observations made with telescopes focused on the full moon have shown processions of birds, one observer estimating that birds passed his point of observation at the rate of 9,000 an hour, which gives some indication of the numbers of birds that are in the air during some of the nights when migration is at its height. While the steady night-long passage of migratory birds has been recorded, the bulk of the flocks pass during the earlier hours of the evening and toward daylight in the morning, the periods from 8 o'clock to midnight and from 4 to 6 a. m. seeming to be favorite times for nocturnal flight.

It has been claimed, with some reason, that small birds migrate by night the better to avoid their enemies, and that most of the nocturnal travelers are those that are naturally timid, sedentary, or feeble-winged. To a certain extent this may be true as included in this group are not only such weak fliers as the rails but also the small song and insectivorous birds such as the wrens, the small woodland flycatchers, and other species which, living habitually more or less in concealment, are probably much safer making their flights under the protecting cloak of darkness. Nevertheless, it must be remembered that night migrants include also the snipe, sandpipers, and plovers, birds that are always found in the open, and are among the more powerful fliers, some of them making flights of more than 2,000 miles across the ocean.

Night travel is probably best for the majority of birds chiefly from the standpoint of feeding. Digestion is very rapid in birds and yet the stomach of one killed during the day almost always contains food. To replace the energy required for long flight, it is essential that food be obtained at comparatively short intervals, the longest of which in most species is during the hours of darkness. If the smaller migrants were to make protracted flights by day they would be likely to arrive at their destination at nightfall almost exhausted, but since they are entirely daylight feeders, they would be unable to obtain food until the following morning. This would delay further flights and result in great exhaustion or possibly even death were they so unfortunate as to have their evening arrival coincident with unusually cold or stormy weather. Traveling at night, they pause at daybreak and devote the entire period of daylight to alternate feeding and resting. This permits complete recuperation and resumption of the journey at nightfall.

Many species of wading and swimming birds migrate either by day or night, as they are able to feed at all hours, and are not accustomed to seek safety in concealment. Some diving birds, including ducks that submerge when in danger, sometimes travel over water by day and over land at night. The day migrants include, in addition to some of the ducks and geese, the loons, cranes, gulls, pelicans, hawks, swallows, nighthawks, and the swifts. All of these are strong-winged birds. The swifts, swallows, and nighthawks (sometimes called bullbats) feed entirely on flying insects, and use their short, weak feet and legs only for grasping a perch during periods of rest or sleep. Thus they feed as they travel, the circling flocks being frequently seen in late summer working gradually southward. Years ago before birds of prey were so thoughtlessly slaughtered, great flocks of red-tailed, Swainson's, and rough-legged hawks might be seen wheeling majestically across the sky in the Plains States, and in the East the flights of broadwinged, Cooper's, and sharp-skinned hawks are still occasionally seen. To the birds of prey and possibly to the gulls also, a day's fasting now and then is no hardship, particularly since they frequently gorge themselves to repletion when opportunity is afforded.

An interesting comparison of the flights of day and night migrants may be made through a consideration of the spring migrations of the blackpolled warbler and the cliff swallow. Both spend the winter in

16

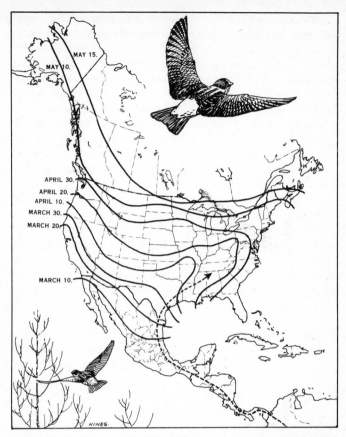

Figure 3.—Migration of the cliff swallow, a day migrant that instead of flying across the Caribbean Sea as does the blackpolled warbler (see fig. 6), follows around the coast of Central America, where food is readily obtained. (See p. 25.)

South America, at which season they are neighbors. But when the impulse comes to start northward toward their respective breeding grounds, the warblers strike straight across the Caribbean Sea to Florida (fig. 6), while the swallows begin their journey by a westward flight of several hundred miles to Panama (fig. 3.). Thence they move leisurely along the western shore of the Caribbean Sea to Mexico, and continuing to avoid a long trip over water, they go completely around the western end of the Gulf of Mexico. This circuitous route adds more than 2,000 miles to the journey of the swallows that nest in Nova Scotia. The question may be asked: "Why should the swallow select a route so much longer and more roundabout than that taken by the blackpolled warbler?" The simple explanation is that the swallow is a day migrant while the warbler travels at night. The migration of the warbler is made up of a series of long, nocturnal flights, alternated with days of rest and feeding in favorable localities. The swallow, on the other hand, starts its migration several weeks earlier and catches each day's ration of flying insects during a few hours of aerial evolutions, which at the same time carry it slowly in the proper direction. Flying along the insect-teeming shores of the Gulf of Mexico, the 2,000 extra miles that are added to the migration route are but a fraction of the distance that these birds cover in pursuit of their daily food.

Although most of our smaller birds make their longest flights at night, close observation will show that travel is continued to some extent by day. This is particularly true during the latter half of a migratory season when the birds show evidence of an overpowering desire to hasten to their breeding grounds. At this time flocks of birds while feeding maintain a movement in the general direction of the seasonal journey. Sometimes they travel hurriedly, and while their flights may be short, they must cover an appreciable distance in the course of a day.

How Birds Migrate

Speed of flight and speed of migration

There is a widespread misconception concerning the speed at which birds normally fly, and even regarding the speed they can attain when occasion demands, as when closely pursued by an enemy. It is not unusual to hear accounts of birds flying "a mile a minute." While undoubtedly some birds can and do attain a speed even greater than this, such cases are exceptional, and it is safe to say that even when pressed, few can develop an air speed of 60 miles an hour. They do, however, have two speeds, one being the normal rate for everyday purposes and also for migration, and an accelerated speed for escape or pursuit; this in some cases may be nearly double the normal rate of movement. Nevertheless, it is doubtful if the effort required for the high speeds could be long sustained, and certainly not for the long-distance migratory journeys that are regularly made by most birds.

The theory that migrating birds attain high speeds received encouragement from the German ornithologist Gätke (1895), who for many years made observations on birds at the island of Heligoland. He postulated that the blue-throat, a species of thrush smaller than the American hermit thrush, would leave African winter quarters at dusk and reach Heligoland at dawn, which would mean a sustained speed of 200 miles an hour, and that the American golden plover flew from the coast of Labrador to Brazil in 15 hours, or at the tremendous speed of 250 miles an hour. Most ornithologists now consider these conclusions to be unwarranted.

Sportsmen also often greatly overestimate the speed at which ducks and geese fly and sometimes attempt to substantiate their estimates by mathematical calculation, based upon the known velocity of a charge of shot, the estimated distance and the estimated "lead" that was necessary to hit the bird. If all three elements of the equation were known with certainty, the speed of the bird could be determined with a fair degree of accuracy. The majority of the ducks that are reported as killed at 40, 50, or even 60 yards, however, actually are shot at distances much less than estimated. To sight along a gun barrel and estimate correctly the distance of a moving object against the sky is so nearly impossible for the average gunner as to make such calculations of little value.

During the past few years reliable data on the speed of birds have accumulated slowly. It has been found that a common flying speed of ducks and geese is between 40 and 50 miles an hour, and that it is much less among the smaller birds. Herons, hawks, horned larks, ravens, and shrikes, timed with the speedometer of an automobile, have been found to fly 22 to 28 miles an hour, while some of the flycatchers are such slow fliers that they attain only 10 to 17 miles an hour. Even such fast-flying birds as the mourning dove rarely exceed 35 miles an hour. All these birds can fly faster, but it is to be remembered that at training camps during World War I, airplanes having a maximum speed of about 80 miles an hour easily overtook flocks of ducks that, it may be supposed, were making every effort to escape. Aviators have claimed that at 65 miles an hour they can overtake the fastest ducks, though cases are on record of ducks passing airplanes that were making 55 miles an hour.

The greatest bird speeds that have been reliably recorded are of the swifts and the duck hawk, or peregrine falcon. An observer in an airplane in Mesopotamia reported that swifts easily circled his ship when it was traveling at 68 miles an hour. To do this, the birds certainly were flying at a speed as high as 100 miles an hour. Once a hunting duck hawk, timed with a stop watch, was calculated to have attained a speed between 165 and 180 miles an hour.

The speed of migration, however, is quite different from that attained in forced flights for short distances. A sustained flight of 10 hours a day would carry herons, hawks, crows, and smaller birds from 100 to 250 miles, while ducks and geese might travel as much as 400 to 500 miles in the same period. Measured as air-line distances, these journeys are impressive and indicate that birds could cover the ordinary migration route from the northern United States or even from northern Canada to winter quarters in the West Indies or in Central America or South America in a relatively short time. It is probable that individual birds do make flights of the length indicated and that barn swallows seen in May on Beata Island, off the southern coast of the Dominican Republic, may have reached that point after a nonstop flight of 350 miles across the Caribbean Sea from the coast of Venezuela. Nevertheless, whether they continue such journeys day after day is doubtful.

It seems more likely that migrations are performed in a leisurely manner, and that after a flight of a few hours the birds pause to feed and rest for one or several days, particularly if they find themselves in congenial surroundings. Some indication of this is found in the records of banded birds, particularly waterfowl. Considering only the shortest intervals that have elapsed between banding in the North and recovery in southern regions, it is found that usually a month or more is taken to cover an air-line distance of a thousand miles. For example, a black duck banded at Lake Scugog, Ontario, was killed 12 days later at Vicksburg, Miss. If the bird was taken shortly after its arrival, the record would indicate an average daily flight of only 83 miles, a distance that could have been covered in about 2 hours' flying time. Among the thousands of banding records obtained in recent years, evidences of such rapid flight are decidedly scarce, for with few exceptions all thousand-mile flights have required 2 to 4 weeks or more. Among sportsmen, the blue-winged teal is well known as a fast-flying duck and quite a few of these banded on Canadian breeding grounds have covered 2,300 to 3,000 miles in a 30-day period. Nevertheless, the majority of those that have traveled to South America were not recovered in that region until 2 or 3 months after they were banded. Probably the fastest flight over a long distance for one of these little ducks was one made by a young male which traveled 3,800 miles from the delta of the Athabaska River, in northern Alberta, Canada, to Maracaibo, Venezuela, in exactly 1 month. This flight was at an average speed of 125 miles per day. The greatest migration speed thus far recorded for any banded bird is that of a lesser yellowlegs banded at North Eastham, Cape Cod, Mass., on August 28, 1935, and killed 6 days later, 1,900 miles away, at Lamentin, Martinique, French West Indies. This bird traveled an average daily distance of more than 316 miles.

It seems certain that migratory journeys are performed at the normal rate of flight, as this would best conserve the strength of the birds and eliminate the fatigue that would result from effort required for great speed. Migrating birds passing lightships and lighthouses, or crossing the face of the moon, have been observed to fly without hurry or evidence of straining to attain high speed.

The speed of migration also is demonstrated by the dates of arrival, particularly during the spring movement. The Canada goose affords a typical example of regular, but slow migration. Its advance northward at this season is at the same rate as the advance of the season (fig. 4). In fact, the isotherm of 35° F. appears to be a governing factor in the speed at which these geese move north, and over their entire trip the vanguard follows closely the advance of this isotherm.

Few species perform such regular migrations, many waiting in their winter homes until spring is well advanced and then moving rapidly to their breeding grounds. Sometimes this advance is so rapid that the later migrants actually catch up with species that for a month or more may have been pressing slowly but steadily northward.

One of the best examples of rapid migration is found in the gray-cheeked thrush. This bird winters in Colombia, Ecuador, Peru, Venezuela, and British Guiana and does not start its northward journey until many other species are well on their way. It does not appear in the United States until the last of April—April 25 near the mouth of the Mississippi, and April 30 in northern Florida (fig. 5). A month later, or by the last week in May, the bird is seen in northwestern Alaska, the 4,000-mile trip from Louisiana having been made at an average speed of about 130 miles a day.

Another example of rapid migration is furnished by the yellow, or summer, warbler. Coming from the Tropics, the birds reach New

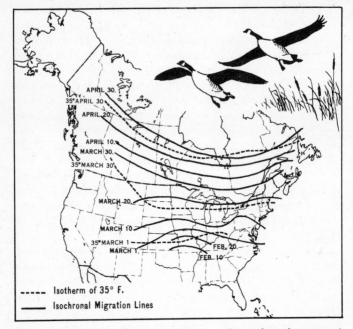

Figure 4.—Migration of the Canada goose. The northward movement keeps pace with the advance of spring, in this case the advance of the isotherm of 35° F. agreeing with that of the birds.

Orleans about April 5, when the average temperature is 65° F. Traveling north much faster than does the season, they reach their breeding grounds in Manitoba the latter part of May, when the average temperature is only 47°. Encountering progressively colder weather over their entire route, they cross a strip of country in the 15 days from May 11 to 25 that spring temperatures take 35 days to cross. This "catching up" with spring is habitual in species that winter south of the United States and in most of the northern species that winter in the Gulf States. To this rule there appear to be only six exceptions—the Canada goose, the mallard, the pintail, the crow, the red-winged blackbird, and the robin.

The blue goose presents a striking example of a late but very rapid spring migration. Practically all members of the species winter in the great coastal marshes of Louisiana, where 50,000 or more may be seen grazing in the "pastures" or flying overhead in flocks of various sizes.

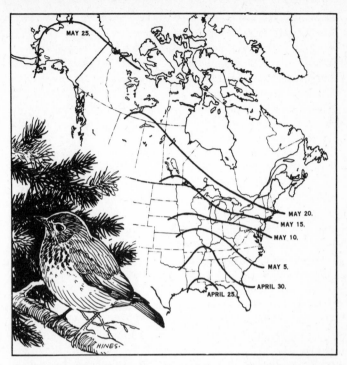

Figure 5.—Isochronal migration lines of the gray-cheeked thrush, an example of rapid migration. The distance from Louisiana to Alaska is about 4,000 miles and is covered at an average speed of about 130 miles a day. The last part of the journey is covered at a speed that is several times what it is in the Mississippi Valley.

Their breeding grounds are chiefly on Baffin Island and on Southampton Island in the northern part of Hudson Bay, in a region where conditions of severe cold prevail except for a few weeks each year. The birds seem to realize that even though the season in their winter quarters is advancing rapidly, their nesting grounds are still covered with a heavy blanket of ice and snow. Accordingly they remain in the coastal marshes until the last of March or the first of April, when the local birds are already busily engaged with the duties of reproduction. The flight northward is rapid, almost nonstop, so far as the United States is concerned, for although the birds are sometimes recorded in large numbers in the Mississippi Valley, including eastern South Dakota, and in southeastern Manitoba, there are few records anywhere along the route of such great flocks as are known to winter in Louisiana. When the birds arrive in the James Bay region of Canada they apparently enjoy a prolonged period of rest, as they are not noted in the vicinity of their breeding grounds until the first of June. During the first 2 weeks of that month they pour into the tundra country by the thousands, and each pair immediately sets about the business of rearing a brood.

The robin has been mentioned as a slow migrant, and as a species it takes 78 days to make the 3,000-mile trip from Iowa to Alaska, a stretch of country that is crossed by advancing spring in 68 days. In this case, however, it does not mean that individual robins are necessarily slow, for probably the northward movement of the species depends upon the continual advance of birds from the rear, the first individuals arriving in a suitable locality remaining to nest, while the northward movement of the species is continued by those still to come.

Special interest attaches to the great variation in the speed at which birds travel in different sections of the broad flyway extending from the Gulf of Mexico to the Arctic Ocean, by way of the Mississippi and Mackenzie Valleys. The blackpolled warbler furnishes an excellent example (fig. 6). This species winters in north-central South America and migrates in April across the West Indies to Florida. From this point some individuals fly northwest to the Mississippi Valley, north to Manitoba, northwest to the Mackenzie River, and thence almost due west to western Alaska. In tracing the long route of these birds it is found that a fairly uniform average speed of 30 to 35 miles a day is maintained from the Gulf to Minnesota. Then comes a spurt, for a week later the blackpolls have reached the central part of the Mackenzie Valley and by the following week they are observed in northwestern Alaska. During the latter part of the journey, therefore, many individuals must average more than 200 miles a day. They use 30 days in traveling from Florida to southern Minnesota, a distance of about 1,000 miles, and scarcely half that time to cover the remaining 2,500 miles to Alaska. It should be noted that the increased speed is directly associated with the change in direction, the north-and-south course in the Mississippi Valley being accomplished slowly while the northwesterly course across Canada is made at a much greater speed. Increased speed across western Canada to Alaska is also shown by many

Figure 6.—Migration of the blackpolled warbler. The solid isochronal lines show the places at which these birds arrive at the same time. As the birds move northward these lines become farther apart, showing that the warblers move faster with the advance of spring. From April 30 to May 10 the average speed is about 30 miles a day, while from May 25 to May 30 it is increased to more than 200 miles.

other birds. A study of all species traveling up the Mississippi Valley indicates an average speed of about 23 miles a day. From southern Minnesota to southern Manitoba 16 species maintain an average speed of about 40 miles a day. From that point to Lake Athabaska, 12 species travel at an average speed of 72 miles a day; while 5 others travel to

Great Slave Lake at 116 miles a day; and another 5 species cover 150 miles a day to reach Alaska. This change is in correlation with a corresponding variation in the isothermal lines, which turn northwestward west of the Great Lakes.

As has been previously indicated, the advance of spring in the northern interior is much more rapid than in the Mississippi Valley and on the Gulf coast. In other words, in the North spring comes with a rush and during the height of the migration season in Saskatchewan the temperature in the southern part of the Mackenzie Valley just about equals that in the Lake Superior area, which is 700 miles farther south. Such conditions, coupled with the diagonal course of the birds across this region of fast-moving spring, exert a great influence on migration and are the chief factors in the acceleration of speed of travel.

Variations in speed of migration in different parts of the country are illustrated also by the movements of the cliff swallow (fig. 3), which breeds from Mexico to Alaska and winters in Brazil and Argentina. It would be expected in spring to appear in the United States first in Florida and Texas then in the southern Rocky Mountain region, and finally on the Pacific coast. As a matter of fact, however, the earliest spring records come from north-central California, where the bird usually is common before the first arrivals are observed in Texas or Florida. The route taken, for many years a migration problem, was solved when it was found that these swallows went around the Gulf of Mexico rather than across it. The isochronal lines on the map show the more rapid advance along the Pacific coast. By March 20, when the vanguard has not quite reached the lower Rio Grande in Texas, the species is already north of San Francisco in California.

Altitude at which birds travel

At one time students of bird migration held firmly to the theory that normal migration takes place at heights above 15,000 feet, reasoning (somewhat uncertainly) that flying becomes easier as altitude is gained. Since the development of the airplane, however, and with it man's exploration of the upper regions of the air, it has become common knowledge that rarified atmosphere adds greatly to the difficulties of flight. This is due not only to the reduction in oxygen (whether for gasoline engine or the lungs of a bird) but also to the lack of buoyancy of the rarified air. Such birds as vultures, pelicans, cranes, and some of the hawks feel this the least, since compared with body weight the supporting surface of their wings is very great, but for the smaller and shorter-winged birds lack of buoyancy at high altitudes presents a difficult obstacle in flight. Even when flying close to the earth, small birds have to keep their wings in rapid motion.

Another postulate favoring the high-altitude flying theory was that the wonderful vision of birds was their sole guidance during migratory flights; and to keep landmarks in view the birds were obliged to fly high, particularly when crossing wide areas of water. This will be considered in greater detail under Orientation (p. 28), so here it will be sufficient to say that birds rely only in part upon vision to guide them on migration. Also, it is to be remembered that there are definite physical limitations to the range of visibility even under perfect atmospheric conditions. Chief of these is the curvature of the earth's surface. Thus, if birds crossing the Gulf of Mexico to Louisiana and Florida flew at a height of 5 miles, they would still be unable to see a third of the way across. And yet this trip is made twice each year by thousands of thrushes, warblers, and others.

Actual knowledge of the altitude of migratory flight is scanty, though estimates obtained by means of the telescope, and still more accurate data resulting from altimeter observation from airplanes, are slowly accumulating. It is, of course, obvious that some birds that cross mountain ranges during migration must attain a great altitude. Observers at an altitude of 14,000 feet in the Himalayas have recorded storks and cranes flying so high that they could be seen only through field glasses. Being beyond the range of unaided vision they must have been at least 6,000 feet above the observers, or at an actual altitude of 20,000 feet above sea level. Such cases, however, are exceptional as aviators have reported that they rarely meet birds above an altitude of 5,000 feet.

It is now known that migration in general is performed below a height of 3,000 feet above the earth. Some proof of this statement is available. Observations made from lighthouses and other points of vantage indicate that migrants commonly travel at altitudes of a very few feet to a few hundred feet above sea or land. Sandpipers, sanderlings, and northern phalaropes, observed in migration on the Pacific oceanic route, have been noted to fly so low that they were visible only as they topped a wave. Observers stationed at lighthouses and lightships off the English coast have similarly recorded the passage of land birds, which sometimes flew just above the surface of the water, and rarely above 200 feet. During the World Wars broad areas in the air were under constant surveillance and among the airplane pilots and observers many took more than a casual interest in birds. Of the several hundred records resulting from their observations only 36 were of birds flying above 5,000 feet, and only 7 above 8,500 feet. Cranes were once recorded at an altitude of 15,000 feet, while the lapwing was the bird most frequently seen at high levels, 8,500 feet being its greatest recorded altitude.

These observations naturally relate only to daytime travelers, but there is no reason to believe that nocturnal migration is performed at higher altitudes. The fact that many birds are killed each year by striking the lanterns at lighthouses, or other man-made obstructions, does not, however, furnish conclusive proof that low altitudes are generally used during nocturnal flight, for it should be recalled that these accidents occur chiefly in foggy or unsettled weather, and also that powerful lights have a great attraction for many species of birds. The altitude at which birds travel is affected by other weather conditions also. For example, flight at the higher elevations is facilitated on clear, warm days by the currents of warm air that ascend from broad areas.

Orientation

There probably is no single aspect of the entire subject of bird migration that challenges our admiration so much as the unerring certainty with which birds cover thousands of miles of land and water to come to rest in exactly the same spot where they spent the previous summer or winter. The records from birds marked with numbered bands offer abundant proof that the same individuals of many species will return again and again to their identical nesting sites. These data show also that many individuals migrate in fall over the same route, year after year, making the same stops and finally arriving at the precise thicket that served them in previous winters.

The faculty that enables these birds to point their course accurately over vast expanses of land and water may, for want of a better term, be called a "sense of direction." Man recognizes this sense in himself, though usually it is imperfect and frequently at fault. Nevertheless the facility with which experienced hunters and woodsmen locate tiny camps or other points in forested or mountainous country, frequently cloaked by darkness or fog, with all recognizable landmarks obliterated seems due to this faculty. Ability to travel with precision over un-marked trails is not limited either to birds or to man. It is likewise possessed by many other mammals as well as by some insects and fishes, the well-known migrations of the salmon and the eel being notable examples.

Ability to follow a more or less definite course to a definite goal is evidently part of an inherited faculty. Both the path and the goal must have been determined either when the habit originated or in the course of its subsequent evolution. The theory is sometimes advanced that the older and more experienced birds lead the way, showing the route to their younger companions. This explanation may be accept-able for some species, but not for those in which adults and the young migrate at different times. The young cowbird that is reared by foster parents flocks with others of its kind when grown and in many cases can hardly be said to have adult guidance in migration. An in-herited migratory instinct with a definite sense of the goal to be reached and the route to be followed must be attributed to these birds.

It is well known that birds possess wonderful vision. If they also have retentive memories subsequent trips over the route may well be steered in part by recognizable landmarks. The arguments against the theory of vision and memory are chiefly that much migration takes place by night and that great stretches of the open sea are crossed with-out hesitation. Nevertheless, the nights are rarely so dark that all terrestrial objects are totally obscured, and such features as coastlines and rivers are just those that are most likely to be seen in the faintest light, particularly by the acute vision of the bird and from its aerial points of observation. But some birds fly unerringly through the densest fog. Members of the Biological Survey, proceeding by steamer from the island of Unalaska to Bogoslof Island in Bering Sea, through a fog that was so heavy as to make invisible every object beyond a hundred yards, recorded the fact that flocks of murres, returning to Bogoslof, after quests for food, broke through the wall of fog astern, flew by the vessel, and disappeared into the mists ahead. The ship was heading direct for the island by the use of compass and chart, but its course was no more sure than that of the birds.

Some investigators have asserted that the sense of direction has its seat in the ears or nasal passages and thus that the bird is enabled to identify air currents and other phenomena. It has been found that disturbance of the columella or the semicircular canals of the inner ear will destroy the homing instinct of the racing pigeon, but experiments in the form of delicate operations, or closing the ears with wax, prove such a serious shock to the sensitive nervous system of the bird that they cannot be considered as affording conclusive evidence. Several years ago careful studies were made of the homing instinct of the sooty and noddy terns, tropical species that in the Atlantic region reach their most northern breeding point on the Dry Tortugas Islands, off the southwest coast of Florida. They are not known to wander regularly any appreciable distance farther north. It was found that some were able to return to their nests on the Tortugas after they had been taken on board ship, confined in cages below decks, and carried northward to distances varying from 400 to 800 miles before being released. Landmarks of all kinds were entirely lacking, and the birds certainly were liberated in a region in which they had had no previous experience.

Possibly the "homing instinct" as shown by these terns, by the man-of-war birds that are trained and used as message carriers in the Tuamotu, Gilbert, and Marshall Islands, and by the homing pigeon, is not identical with the sense of perceptive orientation that figures in the flights of migratory birds. Nevertheless, it seems closely akin and is probably caused by the same impulses, whatever they may be and however they may be received. It should be remembered, however, that while homing may involve flight from a point that the bird has never before visited, the flight is always to a known point—that is, the bird's nest—while, on the other hand, the first migratory flight is always from the region of the bird's birth to a region it has never before visited. The spring migration might, of course, be more nearly considered as true "homing."

Some students have leaned strongly toward the possible existence of a "magnetic sense" as being the important factor in the power of geographical orientation. The theory that migratory birds might be responsive to the magnetic field of the earth was conceived as early as 1855, when some experimental work was done in Russia, and nearly 60 years later in France. Recently investigations in this field have been conducted by Yeagley (1947) and by Gordon (1948) with diametrically opposite results. The idea carries with it the implication that contained in the bird's body is an organ that is sensitive to the effect of its motion through the vertical component of the magnetic field and to other related factors. In the tests by Dr. Yeagley, 20 young homing pigeons were given training flights to their home loft from distances up to 100 miles. Permanent magnets were then affixed to the under side of the manus part of the wings of half of the birds while copper plates of equivalent weight were attached to the wings of the other half. All birds were released singly at an airline distance of about 65 miles from the loft. The results were most suggestive, as only two of the birds carrying magnets returned to the loft, whereas eight of the controls returned.

With certain minor modifications, this experiment was repeated by Gordon. In this case 60 pigeons were used and releases were made from points up to 58 miles, where the direction of flight was such that the birds had to navigate across the gradient of the magnetic field. Every bird returned to its loft on the day of release regardless of whether it carried magnets or unmagnetized bars of the same weight.

Attempts to demonstrate the effect of radio waves on the navigational ability of birds also have produced contradictory results. In some of these tests, homing pigeons released near broadcasting stations have appeared to be hopelessly confused, whereas in others, apparently conducted in the same manner, no effects could be discerned. It is obvious that before the electromagnetic theory can be accepted or rejected, much additional experimental work is necessary.

In concluding this discussion of orientation it is pertinent to point out that the migratory instinct appears to be more or less transitory, that it is not persistent over an extended period. Migratory birds may be arrested en route, either by natural conditions, such as unusual food supplies, or forcibly by the act of man, and detained until the end or nearly the end of the migratory season, and then may not attempt to finish the journey, apparently having lost the migratory impulse. In the fall and early winter of 1929, abundant food and an open season caused an unusual number of mallard ducks to arrest their migration and remain in western Montana and northern Idaho. Later, however, a heavy snowfall with subzero temperatures suddenly cut off the food supply, with the result that great numbers of the birds starved to death, when a flight of a few hours would have carried them to a region of open water and abundant food.

Segregation during migration

During the height of the northward movement in spring the woods and thickets may be suddenly filled with several species of wood warblers, thrushes, sparrows, flycatchers, and others, which it is natural to conclude have traveled together and arrived simultaneously.   Probably they did, but such combined migration is by no means the rule for all species.

As a group the wood warblers (*Compsothlypidae*) probably travel more in mixed companies than do any other single family of North American birds. The flocks are likely to be made up of several species in spring and fall with both adults and young. Sometimes swallows, sparrows, blackbirds, and some of the shore birds also migrate in mixed flocks. In fall, great flocks of blackbirds frequently sweep south across the Plains States, and occasionally one flock will contain bronzed grackles, red-winged blackbirds, yellow-headed blackbirds, and Brewer's blackbirds.

On the other hand many species keep strictly to themselves. It would be difficult for any other kind of bird to keep in company with one of such rapid movements as the chimney swift, which is rarely found associated with any other species at any season. Nighthawks or bullbats also fly in separate companies, as do usually crows, waxwings, crossbills, bobolinks, and kingbirds. Occasionally, a flock of ducks will be observed to contain several species, but generally when they are actually on migration the individuals of each species separate and travel with others of their own kind. The flocks of blue geese, previously mentioned in connection with speed of flight (p. 22), frequently have with them a few of the closely related snow geese, particularly in the eastern part of their winter range. The portion here is usually about 10 to 1, but farther west the numbers of snow geese increase until they outnumber their blue relatives.

The adults of most perching birds drive the young away when they are grown, probably to be relieved of the necessity of providing for them, and also in order that the parents may have opportunity to rest and renew their plumage before starting for winter quarters. The young birds are therefore likely to drift together and, having no further responsibility, may start south ahead of their parents. In contrast with this indifference on the part of the adults of perching birds, Canada geese and some others remain in family groups, the parent birds undergoing the wing molt that renders them flightless during the period of growth of their young, so that old and young acquire their full plumage at the same time and are able to start south together. The large flocks, therefore, are composed of many families that band together, and when they separate into V-shaped units it is probably correct to assume

32

that it is an old bird that leads the group. Where there is segregation of the sexes, the young birds usually accompany their mothers, as is the case with some of the ducks. After the females start to incubate their eggs, the males of most species of ducks flock by themselves and remain together until fall.

The males and females of some species may migrate either simultaneously or separately. In the latter case it is usually the males that arrive first, sometimes great flocks of male birds, as in the red-winged blackbird, reaching a locality several days before any of the females. This is particularly the rule in spring: The first robins are usually found to be males, as are also the first song sparrows, rose-breasted grosbeaks, and scarlet tanagers. This early arrival of the males has been explained on the theory of territorial possession, under which the male selects the area where it elects to breed, each individual attempting to protect a definite territory from trespass by other males of his own kind, at the same time singing or otherwise announcing his presence and inviting the later arriving female to examine the territory that he has selected for nesting. The long-billed marsh wren is a noteworthy example, and the males of this species may enthusiastically build several dummy nests before the females arrive.

In a few species the males and females apparently arrive at the breeding grounds together and proceed at once to nest building. In fact among the shore birds, ducks, and geese, courtship and mating may take place in whole or in part while the birds are in the South or on their way north, so that when they arrive at the northern nesting grounds they are paired and ready to proceed at once with the raising of their families. Mallards and black ducks may be observed in pairs as early as January, the female leading and the male following when they take flight. Naturally these mated pairs migrate north in company, and it was largely to protect such species that duck shooting in spring was abolished by Federal law a number of years ago.

Many shore birds nest well within the Arctic Circle, and it is the opinion of ornithologists that most of these birds share, at least in part, the habits of the phalaropes, a family in which the male assumes the entire care of the eggs and young. If this be true, it explains why in southern latitudes so many of the earliest fall arrivals are females that may have deserted the breeding grounds after the eggs were laid.

Migratory flights are frequently accomplished in close flock formation, as with the shore birds, blackbirds, and waxwings, and especially some of the sparrows—the snow buntings, longspurs, juncos, and tree sparrows. Other species, however, though they travel in flocks, maintain a very loose formation; examples are the turkey vultures, the hawks, swifts, blue jays, swallows, warblers, and bluebirds. Still others, the grebes, great horned owls, winter wrens, shrikes, and belted kingfishers for example, ordinarily travel alone and when several are found in close proximity it is an indication that they have been drawn together by unusual conditions, such as abundant food.

Where Birds Migrate

Definite evidence shows that both the length and the duration of the migratory journey vary greatly. The bobwhite and the western quails, the cardinal, the Carolina wren, and probably some of the titmice and woodpeckers, which are apparently almost or quite non-migratory, may round out their full period of existence without at any time going more than 10 miles from the nest where they were hatched.

Short and undetermined migrations

Song sparrows, meadow larks, blue jays, and some other species make such short migrations that the movement is difficult to detect, as individuals may be found in one area throughout the year. Thus, at the southern part of the range there is merely a concentration in winter, the summer individuals being entirely sedentary. Speculation is useless on the distances of individual migration without definite evidence concerning the precise winter quarters of birds that summer in a particular part of the breeding range of the species, but from the records of banded birds important evidence is becoming available. Eventually it may be possible to say definitely just how far the song sparrows that nest in northern New England and the Maritime Provinces of Canada travel to their winter quarters, and whether the blue jays of New York and the upper Mississippi Valley remain throughout the winter in their breeding areas, or move farther south and relinquish their places to individuals from southern Canada.

An illustration of what is now known on this subject is found in the case of the robin. This bird occurs in the Middle Atlantic States throughout the year, in Canada only in summer, and along the Gulf coast only as a winter resident. On the Atlantic coast its movements are readily ascertained, since, for example, in the section about Washington, D. C., the breeding robin is the southern variety (*Turdus migratorius archrusterus*) which is found there from the first of April to the last of October, when its place is taken (in smaller numbers) by the northern robin (*Turdus migratorius migratorius*), which arrives about the middle of October and remains until the following April. It is probable that a similar interchange of individual robins occurs throughout a large part of the balance of its range, the hardy birds from the north being the winter tenants in the abandoned summer homes of the southern birds.

The red-winged blackbirds that nest in northern Texas are almost sedentary, but in winter they are joined by representatives of other subspecies that nest as far north as the Mackenzie Valley.

Variable migrations within species

The difference in characters between subspecies has been used by students of migration to discover other interesting facts concerning variations of the migratory flight between closely related birds that breed in different latitudes. The familiar eastern fox sparrow (*Passerella iliaca iliaca*) breeds from northwestern Alaska to Labrador, and in winter is found concentrated in the southeastern part of the United States. It thus travels a long distance each year. On the west coast of the continent, however, six subspecies of this bird breed in rather sharply delimited ranges, extending from the region of Puget Sound and Vancouver Island to Unimak Island, at the end of the Alaskan Peninsula. One of these, known as the sooty fox sparrow (*P. i. fuliginosa*) breeds in the Puget Sound area and makes practically no migration at all, while the other races, nesting on the coast of British Columbia and Alaska, are found in winter chiefly in California. The races that breed farthest north are in winter found farthest south, illustrating a tendency for those birds that are forced to migrate to pass over those so favorably located that they have no need to leave their breeding areas, while the northern birds settle for the winter in the unoccupied areas farther south (fig. 7).

Another example of the same kind is the Maryland yellowthroat of the Atlantic coast. Birds occupying the most southern part of the general range are almost nonmigratory, residing throughout the year in Florida, while those breeding as far north as Newfoundland go to the West Indies for the winter, thus passing directly over the home of their southern relatives.

Figure 7.—Migration of Pacific-coast forms of the fox sparrow. The breeding ranges of the different races are encircled by solid lines, while the winter ranges are dotted. The numbers indicate the areas used by the different subspecies, as follows: 1. Shumagin fox sparrow; 2. Kodiak fox sparrow; 3. Valdez fox sparrow; 4. Yakutat fox sparrow; 5. Townsend fox sparrow; 6. Sooty fox sparrow (After Swarth, courtesy of the Museum of Vertebrate Zoology, University of California).

The palm warbler (*Dendroica palmarum*) which breeds from Nova Scotia and Maine west and northwest to southern Mackenzie, has been separated into two subspecies. Those breeding in the interior of Canada (*D. p. palmarum*) make a 3,000-mile journey from Great Slave Lake to Cuba, passing through the Gulf States early in October. After the bulk have passed, the palm warblers from the Northeastern States and Provinces (*D. p. hypochrysea*) drift slowly into the Gulf Coast region, where they remain for the winter. Their migratory journey is about half as long as that of the northwestern subspecies.

There is no invariable law governing the distance of migration, although in general it is found that where a species has an extensive range, the subspecies that breed farthest north go farthest south to spend the winter.

Fall flights not far south of breeding ranges

Some other species that have extensive summer ranges, for instance the pine warbler, rock wren, field sparrow, loggerhead shrike, and black-headed grosbeak, are found to concentrate during the winter season in the southern part of the breeding range, or to occupy additional territory that is only a short distance farther south. The entire species may thus be confined within a restricted area for the period of winter, and then, with the return of warmer weather, spreads out to reoccupy the full range.

There are many species, including the tree sparrow, slate-colored junco, and Lapland longspur, that nest in Canada and winter in the United States; while others, including the vesper sparrow, chipping sparrow, grackles, red-winged blackbirds, bluebirds, the woodcock, and several species of ducks, nest in the northern United States and move south for the winter to areas along the Gulf of Mexico. This list includes the more hardy species, some individuals of which may linger in protected places well within the reach of severe cold, as, for example, Wilson's snipe or jacksnipe, which frequently is found during subzero weather in parts of the Rocky Mountain region where warm springs assure a food supply. More than 100 of our summer birds leave the United States entirely and spend the winter in the West Indies, or in Central America or South America. For example, the Cape May warbler, which breeds from northern New England, northern Michigan, and northern Minnesota, north to New Brunswick, Nova Scotia, and nearly to Great Slave Lake, is concentrated in winter chiefly in the West Indies, its metropolis at this season being the island of Hispaniola.

Long-distance migrations

Some of the common summer residents are not content with a trip to northern South America, but push on across the Equator and finally come to rest for the winter in the pampas of Argentina, or even in Patagonia. Thus some species that are more or less associated with each other in summer, as nighthawks, barn swallows, cliff swallows, and some of the thrushes, may also occupy the same general winter quarters in Brazil. Some individual nighthawks and barn swallows travel still farther, and of all North American land birds these species probably have the longest migration route, as they occur north in summer to Yukon and Alaska, and south in winter to Argentina, 7,000 miles away. Such seasonal flights are exceeded in length, however, by the journeys of several species of water birds, chiefly members of the suborder of shore birds. In this group there are 19 species that breed north of the Arctic Circle and winter in South America, 6 of them going as far south as Patagonia, and thus having a migration route more than 8,000 miles in length.

The arctic tern is the champion "globe trotter" and long-distance flier (fig. 8). Its name "arctic" is well earned, as its breeding range is circumpolar and it nests as far north as it can find a suitable place. The first nest to be found in this region was only 7½ degrees from the North Pole, and it contained a downy chick surrounded by a wall of newly fallen snow that had been scooped out by the parent. In North America the arctic tern breeds south in the interior to Great Slave Lake, and on the Atlantic coast to Massachusetts. After the young are grown the arctic terns disappear from their North American breeding grounds, and a few months later they may be found in the Antarctic region, 11,000 miles away. Until very recently the route followed by these hardy fliers was a complete mystery, for although a few scattered individuals have been noted south as far as Long Island, the species is otherwise practically unknown along the Atlantic coasts of North America and South America. It is, however, known as a migrant on the west coast of Europe and Africa. By means of numbered bands the picture is now developing of what is apparently not only the longest but also one of the most remarkable of all migratory journeys.

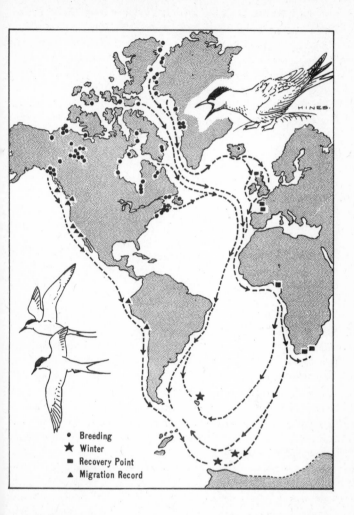

- • Breeding
- ★ Winter
- ■ Recovery Point
- ▲ Migration Record

Figure 8.—Distribution and migration of the arctic terns of eastern North America. The route indicated for this bird is unique, as no other species is known to breed abundantly in North America and to cross the Atlantic Ocean to and from the Old World. The extreme summer and winter homes are 11,000 miles apart, and as the route taken is circuitous, these terns probably fly at least 25,000 miles each year.

Judging by the evidence at present available it seems likely that the arctic terns of eastern North America originally found their way here from the Old World, probably by way of Iceland and Greenland. Consequently when the time comes for them to migrate to winter quarters they do not go directly south as do the common and Forster's terns, but instead they fly back eastward along their ancestral route across the Atlantic to the shores of Europe and then go south along the African coast to their winter home. Those that breed in the northwestern part of the continent, as in Alaska, probably migrate chiefly down the western coast, as the species is not infrequently reported on the coast of California and also on the western coast of South America.

The evidence yielded by banding consists of only six definite cases, but their interpretation permits but one conclusion. All were banded either as downy chicks or as nonflying immature birds. The details of their banding and recovery are of sufficient interest to justify citing in detail. The first was banded on July 3, 1913, at Eastern Egg Rock, Maine,[2] and in August 1917 was found dead in the Niger River delta, West Africa. The second was banded at the Red Islands, Turnevik Bay, Labrador, on July 22, 1927, and was recovered near La Rochelle, France, on October 1, 1927. The third, also banded on the Red Islands, on July 23, 1928, was retaken at Margate, near Port Shepstone, Natal, South Africa, on November 14, 1928. The fourth, banded at Machias Seal Island, New Brunswick, on July 20, 1935, was captured near St. Nazaire, France, October 8, 1935. The fifth and sixth were banded at Machias Seal Island also; the fifth, banded July 5, 1947, was found on November 10, 1948, at Kingfisher Creek, Sedgefield, near Wilderness, Eastern Cape Province, South Africa, while the sixth, banded on July 18, 1948, was picked up dead during the latter part of September 1948 on the hills near Kyle Strome, Sutherland, Scotland. All that remained of the bird that provides the last-named case was a mutilated foot and it appeared that it had been the victim of some predator. It should be pointed out that the flights indicated in the third and fifth cases detailed above, are the longest known for any birds. Both are between 8,000 and 9,000 miles, which in the case of No. 3 was accomplished in less than 3 months.

Probably no other animal in the world enjoys as many hours of daylight as does the arctic tern, since for these birds the sun never sets

---

[2] Recorded at the time of banding as a common tern, a natural error, as the downy young of common and arctic terns look almost exactly alike.

during the nesting season in the northern part of the range, while during their sojourn in the south, daylight is continuous. During several months of the year they have 24 hours of daylight and during the other months considerably more daylight than darkness.

Routes of Migration

While it is beyond question that certain general directions of flight are constantly followed by migratory birds, it is well to remember that the term "migration route" is to some extent a theoretical concept concerned entirely with the lines of general advance or retreat of a species, rather than the exact course followed by individual birds. Even the records of banded birds usually show no more than the place of banding and recovery, and one must have recourse to intermediate records and to reasoning based on probabilities to fill in details of the route actually traversed between the two points.

There is also infinite variety in the routes covered during migration by different species. In fact, the choice of migration highways is so wide that it seems as if the routes of no two species coincide. Differences in distance traveled, time of starting, speed of flight, geographical position, latitudes of breeding and of wintering grounds, and in other factors, all contribute to this great variation of migration routes. Nevertheless, there are certain factors that serve to guide the avian travelers along more or less definite lines, and it is possible to define general lines of migration for the majority of species.

It has been frequently observed that migrating birds have a tendency to follow major topographic lines on the earth's surface when their trend is in the general direction of the birds' journey. Bird migration is generally thought of as a north-and-south movement, with the lanes of heavier concentration following the coasts, mountain ranges, and principal river valleys. To a considerable extent this is the case, particularly in North America, where the coast lines, mountain chains, and larger rivers in general run north and south. In cases where the migration is a long one, however, the notion must be abandoned that the birds' flight is always restricted to narrow routes that follow river valleys and the like, as many species seem to disregard utterly such apparently good natural highways. For example, the Arkansas River has a general east-and-west course for a great part of its length, and while it does constitute a route for many perching birds en route from the Mississippi Valley to the Rocky Mountain region, some of the hawks and many ducks and shore birds pay the valley scant attention. They may arrest the autumn journey to feed among the cottonwoods or along sand bars, but when ready to resume their flight they leave the river and fly directly south over the more or less arid region that lies between the Arkansas and the Rio Grande.

Wide and narrow migration lanes

When birds start their southward migration the movement necessarily involves the full width of the breeding range. Later there is a convergence of the lines of flight taken by individual birds, owing to the conformation of the land mass, and as the species proceeds southward the width of the occupied region becomes less and less. An example of this is provided by the common kingbird, which breeds from Newfoundland to British Columbia, a summer range 2,800 miles wide. On migration, however, its paths converge until in the southern part of the United States the occupied area extends from Florida to the mouth of the Rio Grande, a distance of only 900 miles, and still farther south the migration path is further restricted. In the latitude of Yucatan it is not more than 400 miles wide, and it is probable that the great bulk of the species moves in a belt that is less than half that width.

A migration route, therefore, may be anything from a narrow path that adheres closely to some definite geographical feature, such as a river valley or a coast line, to a broad boulevard that leads in the desired direction and which follows only the general trend of the land mass. Also it is to be remembered that whatever main routes are described, there remains a multitude of tributary and separate minor routes. In fact, with the entire continent of North America crossed by migratory birds, the different groups or species frequently follow lines that may repeatedly intersect those taken by others of their own kind or by other species. The arterial routes, therefore, must be considered merely as indicating paths of migration on which the tendency to concentrate is particularly noticeable.

In considering the width of migration lanes it will be obvious that certain species, as the knot and the purple sandpiper, which are normally found only along the coasts, must have extremely narrow routes of travel. They are limited on one side by the broad waters of the ocean, and on the other by land and fresh water, both of which are unsuited to furnish the food that is desired and necessary to the well-being of these species.

Figure 9.—Breeding and wintering ranges and migration of Harris's sparrow, an example of a narrow migration route through the interior of the country. The heavy broken lines enclose the region traversed by the majority of these finches; the light broken line encloses the country where they occur with more or less regularity; while the spots indicate records of accidental or sporadic occurrence.

Among land birds that have a definite migration, the Ipswich sparrow has what is probably the most restricted migration range of any species. It is known to breed only on Sable Island, Nova Scotia, and it winters along the Atlantic coast south to Georgia. Living constantly within sound of the surf, it is rarely more than a quarter of a mile from the outer beach, and is entirely at home among the sand dunes and their sparse covering of coarse grass.

Harris's sparrow supplies an interesting example of a narrow migration route in the interior of the country (fig. 9.) This fine, large finch is known to breed only in the region from Churchill, on the west shore of Hudson Bay, northwest to the shores of Great Bear Lake. Very

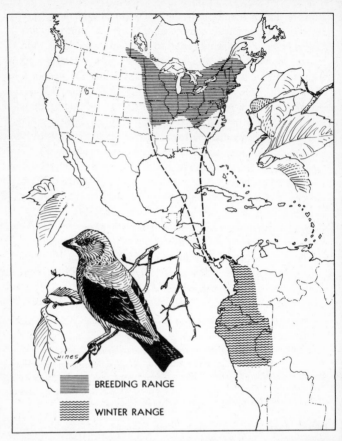

BREEDING RANGE

WINTER RANGE

Figure 10.—Distribution and migration of the scarlet tanager. During the breeding season individual scarlet tanagers may be 1,900 miles apart in an east-and-west line across the breeding range. In migration, however, the lines converge until in southern Central America they are not more than 100 miles apart. For migration paths of other widths see figures 9, 11, and 12.

few actual breeding records of the species are available, but these are sufficient to indicate that the breeding range is in the strip of country characterized by more or less stunted timber just south of the limit of trees. When it begins its fall migration, this species necessarily covers the full width of its breeding area. Then it proceeds almost directly south, or slightly southeasterly, the area covered by the majority of the birds becoming gradually constricted, so that by the time it reaches the United States it is most numerous in a belt about 500 miles wide, extending across North Dakota to central Minnesota. Harris's sparrows are noted on migration with fair regularity east to the western shore of Lake Michigan, and west to the foothills of the Rocky Mountains, but the great bulk of the species moves north and south through a relatively narrow path in the central part of the continent. Present knowledge suggests that the reason for this narrow migration range is the close association that Harris's sparrow maintains with a certain type of habitat including brushy places, thickets, edges of groves, and weed patches. While these environmental conditions are found in other parts of the country, the region crossed by this sparrow presents almost a continuous succession of habitat of this type. Its winter range extends from southeastern Nebraska and northwestern Missouri, across eastern Kansas and Oklahoma and through a narrow section of central Texas, at places hardly more than 150 miles wide.

The scarlet tanager presents another extreme case of narrowness of migration route (fig. 10), its breeding range extending in greatest width from New Brunswick to Saskatchewan, a distance of about 1,900 miles. As the birds move southward in fall their path of migration becomes more and more constricted, until at the time they leave the United States all are included in the 600-mile belt from eastern Texas to the Florida peninsula. Continuing to converge through Honduras and Costa Rica, the boundaries there are not more than 100 miles apart. The species winters in northwestern South America, where it spreads out over most of Colombia, Ecuador, and Peru.

The rose-breasted grosbeak also leaves the United States through the 600-mile stretch from eastern Texas to Apalachicola Bay, but thereafter the lines do not further converge, as this grosbeak enters the northern part of its winter quarters in Central America and South America through a door of about the same width (fig. 11).

Although the cases cited represent extremes of convergence, a narrowing of the migratory path is the rule to a greater or less degree for the majority of North American birds. The shape of the continent tends to effect this, and so the width of the migration route in the latitude of the Gulf of Mexico is usually much less than in the breeding territory.

The redstart represents a notable case of a wide migration route, although even in the southern United States this is much narrower than

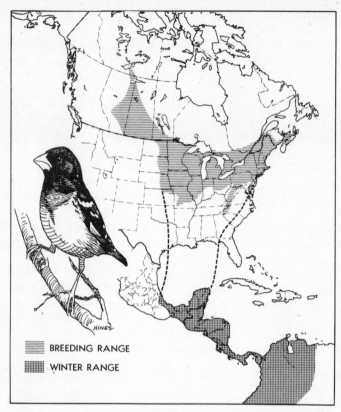

Figure 11.—Distribution and migration of the rose-breasted grosbeak.
Though the width of the breeding range is about 2,500 miles, the
migratory lines converge until the boundaries are only about 700
miles apart when the birds leave the United States.   For migration
paths of other widths see figures 9, 10, and 12.

the breeding range (fig. 12).   These birds, however, cross all parts of
the Gulf of Mexico and pass from Florida to Cuba and Haiti by way of
the Bahamas, so that here their route has a width of about 2,500 miles.

The flyways

In 1935, as a result of studies of banding data, the author discovered
the existence of the four great flyway systems.   This discovery, based

Figure 12.—**Distribution and migration of the redstart.** An example of a wide migration route, since birds of this species cross all parts of the Gulf of Mexico, or may travel from Florida to Cuba and through the Bahamas. Their route thus has an east-and-west width of more than 2,000 miles. For migration paths of greater or less extent see figures 9, 10, and 11.

upon analyses of the several thousand records of the recovery of migratory waterfowl then available, was announced by the Biological Survey (Lincoln, 1935c) and, beginning in 1948, it has served as the basis for administrative action by the Fish and Wildlife Service in the annual hunting regulations.

Although this study was confined to this one family of birds there is a growing mass of evidence in support of the belief that all populations of migratory birds adhere with more or less fidelity to their respective flyways. The terms "flyway" and "migration route" have in the past been used more or less as synonyms but the modern concept of a flyway is that it is a vast geographic region with extensive breeding grounds and wintering grounds connected with each other by a more or less complicated system of migration routes. Each flyway has its own populations of birds, even of those species that may have a continental distribution. The breeding grounds of one or more flyways may (and usually do) overlap broadly, so that during the nesting season extensive areas may be occupied by birds of the same species but which belong to different flyways.

The maps (figs. 13, 14, 15, and 16) show the flyways as they are now understood. It should be pointed out, however, that in the other maps used in this bulletin, the entire range of a species is shown without any attempt to distinguish by flyways the different populations. As banding data accumulate for the nongame species, this distinction will ultimately be possible, but for the time being, consideration of their migrations must be chiefly by routes.

The following discussion of the principal routes of North American birds relates chiefly to the fall migration, for, except as otherwise noted, the spring flight generally retraces the same course. The routes indicated on the map (fig. 17) must not be considered as representing paths with clearly defined borders, but rather as convenient subdivisions of the four great flyways that, as indicated above, cover practically the entire width of the North American Continent and extend from the Arctic coast to South America.

Atlantic oceanic route

By reference to figure 17 it will be noted that route No. 1 is almost entirely oceanic, passing directly over the Atlantic Ocean from Labrador and Nova Scotia to the Lesser Antilles, and then through this group of small islands to the mainland of South America. This is not a popular route and its chief claim to fame is that it is the fall route used by most of the adult eastern golden plovers, and probably by some other shore birds. Since it lies entirely over the sea, this route is definitely known only at its terminals and from occasional observations made on Bermuda and other islands in its course. Some of the shore birds that breed on the Arctic tundra of Mackenzie and Alaska fly southeastward across Canada to the Atlantic coast and finally follow this

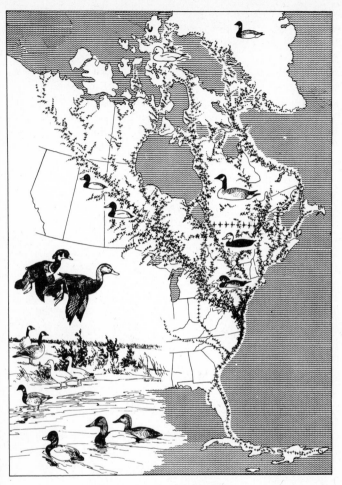

Figure 13.—The Atlantic flyway.

oceanic route to the mainland of South America. The golden plover may accomplish the whole 2,400 miles without pause or rest, in fair weather the flocks passing Bermuda and sometimes even the islands of the Antilles without stopping. Although most birds make their migratory flights either by day or by night, the golden plover in this

Figure 14.—The Mississippi flyway.

remarkable journey flies both day and night. As it swims lightly and easily it may make a few short stops along the way, and it has been seen actually resting on the ocean. Other shore birds have been observed busily feeding in the great area of ocean known as the Sargasso Sea, where thousands of square miles of floating seaweed teem with marine life.

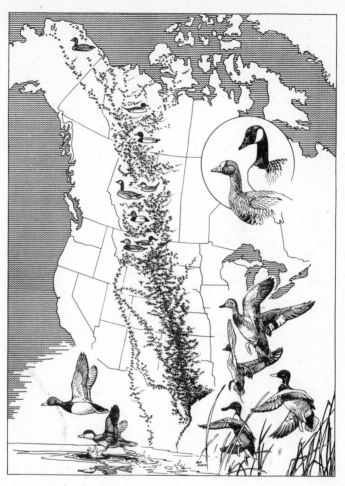

Figure 15.—The Central flyway.

The annual flight of the adult eastern golden plover is so wonderful that it may be given in some detail, particularly since it is one of the exceptions to the general rule that spring and fall movements are over the same routes (fig. 18). After reaching the South American coast the birds make a short stop and then continue overland to the pampas

51

Figure 16.—The Pacific flyway.

of Argentina, where they remain from September to March. Leaving
their winter quarters, they cross northwestern South America and the
Gulf of Mexico, reaching the North American mainland on the coasts
of Texas and Louisiana. Thence they proceed slowly up the Mississippi
Valley, and by the early part of June are again on their breeding
grounds, having performed a round-trip journey in the form of an

enormous ellipse with the minor axis about 2,000 miles and the major axis 8,000 miles, reaching from the Arctic tundra to the pampas of Argentina. The older birds are probably accompanied by some of the young, perhaps those from early nestings, but most of the immature birds leave their natal grounds late in summer and move southward through the interior of the country, returning in spring over essentially the same course. The elliptical route is therefore used chiefly by fully adult birds.

Atlantic coast route and tributaries

The Atlantic coast is a regular avenue of travel, and along it are many famous points for observing both land and water birds. About 50 different kinds of land birds that breed in New England follow the

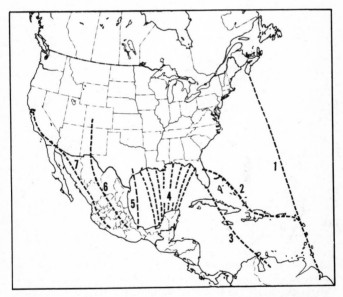

Figure 17.—Principal migration routes used by birds in passing from North America to winter quarters in the West Indies, Central America, and South America. Route No. 4 is the one used most extensively; only a few species make the 2,400-mile flight from Nova Scotia to South America.

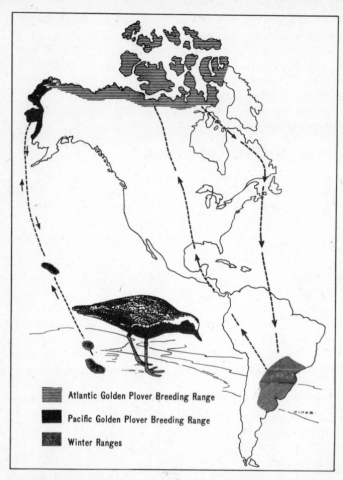

Atlantic Golden Plover Breeding Range

Pacific Golden Plover Breeding Range

Winter Ranges

Figure 18.—Distribution and migration of the golden plover. Adults of the eastern form migrate across northeastern Canada and then by a nonstop flight reach South America. In spring they return by way of the Mississippi Valley. Their entire route is therefore in the form of a great ellipse with a major axis of 8,000 miles and a minor axis of about 2,000 miles. The Pacific golden plover, which breeds in Alaska, apparently makes a nonstop flight across the ocean to Hawaii, the Marquesas Islands, and the Low Archipelago, returning in spring over the same route.

coast southward to Florida and travel thence by island and mainland to South America (fig. 17, route 2). As will be seen from the map, a seemingly natural and convenient highway extends through the Bahamas, Cuba, Hispaniola, Puerto Rico, and the Lesser Antilles to the South American coast. Resting places are afforded at convenient intervals, and at no time need the aerial travelers be out of sight of land. It is not, however, the favored highway, and only about 25 species of birds go beyond Cuba to Puerto Rico along this route to their winter quarters, while only 6 species are known to reach South America by way of the Lesser Antilles. The obvious draw-back is lack of adequate food. The total area of all the West Indies east of Puerto Rico is less than that of Rhode Island, so that if only a small part of the birds of the eastern United States were to travel this way, it is doubtful whether even the luxuriant flora and fauna of tropical habitats would provide food sufficient for their needs. Nevertheless, many thousands of coots, widgeons, pintails, blue-winged teal, and other waterfowl and shorebirds regularly spend the winter season in the coastal marshes and the inland lakes and ponds of Cuba, Hispaniola, and Puerto Rico.

The map (fig. 17) also will show that route No. 3 presents a direct line of travel for Atlantic coast migrants en route to South America, although it involves much longer flights. It is used almost entirely by land birds. After taking off from the coast of Florida there are only two intermediate land masses where the migrants may pause for rest and food. Nevertheless, tens of thousands of birds of some 60 species cross the 150 miles from Florida to Cuba where about half this number elect to remain for the winter months. The others do not hesitate to fly the 90 miles between Cuba and Jamaica, but from that point to the South American coast there is a stretch of islandless ocean fully 500 miles across. Scarcely a third of the North American migrants leave the forested mountains of Jamaica to risk the perils of this ocean trip. Chief among these is the bobolink, which so far outnumbers all other birds using this route that it may be well called the "bobolink route" (fig. 19). As traveling companions along this route, the bobolink may meet a vireo, a kingbird, and a nighthawk from Florida; the chuck-wills-widow of the Southeastern States; the black-billed and the yellow-billed cuckoos from New England; the gray-cheeked thrush from Quebec; bank swallows from Labrador; and the blackpolled warbler from Alaska. Sometimes this scattered assemblage will be joined by a tanager or a wood thrush but the "bobolink

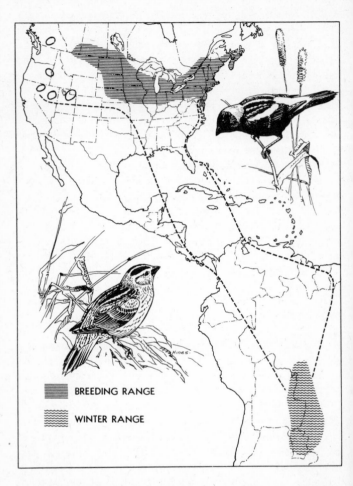

BREEDING RANGE

WINTER RANGE

Figure 19.—Distribution and migration of the bobolink. In crossing to South America most of the bobolinks use route 3 (fig. 17), showing no hesitation in making the flight from Jamaica across an islandless stretch of ocean. It will be noted that colonies of these birds have established themselves in western areas, but in migration they adhere to the ancestral flyways and show no tendency to take the short cut across Arizona, New Mexico, and Texas. (See p. 55.)

route" is not popular with the greater number of migrants, and although many individuals traverse it, they are only a small fraction of the multitudes of North American birds that spend the winter in South America.

Formerly it was thought that most of the North American land birds that migrate to Central America made a leisurely trip along the Florida coast, crossed to Cuba, and thence made the short flight from the western tip of Cuba to Yucatan. A glance at the map would suggest this as a most natural route, but as a matter of fact it is practically deserted except for a few swallows and shorebirds, or an occasional land bird storm-driven from its accustomed course. What actually happens is that in the fall many of the birds that breed east of the Allegheny Mountains travel parallel to the seacoast in a more or less southwesterly direction and, apparently maintaining this same general course from northwestern Florida, cross the Gulf of Mexico to the coastal regions of eastern Mexico.

The routes used by the Atlantic brant merit some detail for the reason that these were long misunderstood. These birds winter on the Atlantic coast, chiefly at Barnegat Bay, N. J., but (depending upon the severity of the season and the food available) south also to North Carolina. Their breeding grounds are in the Canadian arctic archipelago and on the coasts of Greenland. According to the careful studies of Lewis (1937), the main body travels northward in spring along the coast to the Bay of Fundy, hence overland to Northumberland Strait, which separates Prince Edward Island from the mainland of New Brunswick and Nova Scotia. A minor route appears to lead northward from Long Island Sound by way of such valleys as those of the Housatonic and Connecticut Rivers, and on across southern Quebec to the St. Lawrence River.

After spending the entire month of May feeding and resting in various parts of the Gulf of St. Lawrence, the eastern segment of the brant population suddenly resumes its journey by crossing to the north shore of the St. Lawrence estuary. The Bay of Seven Islands, in this general region, is the point of departure for long overland flights that are made by the two segments of the population. The eastern and larger of these appears to fly almost due north to Ungava Bay and from there to nesting grounds, probably in Baffin Island and Greenland. The smaller segment travels a route that is but slightly north of west to the southeastern shores of James Bay, although somewhere to the east of that area some of the flocks take a more northwesterly course, descending the Fort George River to reach the eastern shore of James Bay about two-thirds of the distance north of its southern extremity. Upon their arrival at either of these two points on James Bay, the brant of this western segment turn northward and proceed through the eastern part of Hudson Bay to their breeding grounds, probably in western Baffin Island, Southampton Island, and other islands in the Canadian Arctic.

In general, the fall migration of the brant follows the routes utilized in the spring. At this season, when gathering for the flight of 570 miles to the St. Lawrence River, they appear only on the western and southern shores of Ungava Bay. Also, it appears that most of the birds of the western segment, instead of following the eastern shores of Hudson and James Bays, turn southwestward across the former, by way of the Belcher Islands, to Cape Henrietta Maria and from there south along the western shores of James Bay by way of Akimiski and Charlton Islands. At the southern end of James Bay they are joined by those that have taken the more direct route along the east coasts of the bays and all then fly overland 570 miles to the estuary of the St. Lawrence River.

The Atlantic flyway receives accretions of waterfowl from three or four interior migration paths, one of which is of first importance, as it includes great flocks of canvasbacks, redheads, scaup ducks, Canada geese, and many of the black ducks that winter in the waters and marshes of the coastal region south of Delaware Bay. The canvasbacks, redheads, and scaups come from their breeding grounds on the great northern plains of central Canada, follow the general southeasterly trend of the Great Lakes, cross Pennsylvania over the mountains, and reach the Atlantic coast in the vicinity of Delaware and Chesapeake Bays. Black ducks, mallards, and blue-winged teals that have gathered in southern Ontario during the fall leave these feeding grounds and proceed southwest over a course that is apparently headed for the Mississippi Valley. Many do continue this route down the Ohio Valley, but others, upon reaching the vicinity of the St. Clair Flats, between Michigan and Ontario, swing abruptly to the southeast and, crossing the mountains in a single flight, reach the Atlantic coast south of New Jersey. This route, with its Mississippi Valley branch, has been fully demonstrated by the recovery records of ducks banded at Lake Scugog, Ontario.

The white-winged scoter, which also breeds in the interior of the continent from northern North Dakota north to the Arctic coast, was at one time credited with an elliptical migration route, at least insofar as those wintering on the Atlantic coast are concerned. This sea duck nests only near fresh water but spends the winters on the ocean along both the Atlantic and Pacific coasts of the United States. It migrates over land surfaces mainly at night and it is now believed that after working northward to the waters of Long Island Sound it starts up the valleys of the Hudson and Connecticut Rivers and flies overland to the Great Lakes, from which region it continues west and north-west to the breeding grounds, returning to its winter quarters over the same route. Early ideas alleging an elliptical route probably arose from the fact that great numbers of first-year nonbreeding birds regu-larly pass up the New England coast, cross the Gulf of St. Lawrence and spend the summer loafing off the coast of Labrador. In the fall these birds form into large flocks and retrace their flight, chiefly during daylight hours, to winter quarters from southeastern Maine south at least to Chesapeake Bay. As it was not known that the white-winged scoter does not usually breed until it is 2 years old, and since the south-ward movement of yearling birds was conspicuous while the travels of those from the nesting grounds were chiefly at night, the theory was advanced that the latter flew 1,500 miles due east from the region west of Hudson Bay to the coast of Labrador, thence southward to the known winter quarters.

A study of the Canada geese that winter abundantly in the waters of Back Bay, Va., and Currituck Sound, N. C., reveals another im-portant tributary to the Atlantic coast route. Banding has shown that the principal breeding grounds of these birds are among the islands and on the eastern shore of Hudson Bay. From this region they move south in autumn to the point of Lower Ontario between Lakes Erie and Huron. Occasionally one of these geese will be recovered in the Mississippi Valley but the great majority are retaken either on their breeding grounds or on the Atlantic coast south of Delaware Bay, showing another instance of a long cross-country flight by waterfowl. Although the Canada goose is abundant in migration on the coast of New England, the birds taken there rarely include any of those banded in southern Ontario. The northeastern population of these geese comes from breeding areas in New England, the Maritime Provinces of Canada, Newfoundland, and the desolate coast of Labrador, their migration being entirely coastwise. Still another cross-country route between the Mississippi Valley and the Atlantic coast remains to be briefly described. It is not yet well understood, but the banding of ducks such as the blue-winged teal on the coastal saw-grass marshes of South Carolina has revealed that there is a migration route across the Appalachians to the Mississippi Valley. Birds marked in these marshes have been retaken in Tennessee and Kentucky, as well as in other States farther north in the Mississippi Flyway.

Mackenzie Valley–Great Lakes–Mississippi Valley route and tributaries

Easily the longest route of any in the Western Hemisphere is that extending from the Mackenzie Valley past the Great Lakes and down the Mississippi River, including its tributaries. Its northern terminus is on the Arctic coast in the regions of Kotzebue Sound, Alaska, and the mouth of the Mackenzie River, while its southern end lies in Patagonia. During the spring migration some of the shore birds traverse the full extent of this great path, and it seems likely that the night-hawk, the barn swallow, the blackpolled warbler, and individuals of several other species that breed north to Yukon and Alaska must twice each year cover the larger part of it.

For more than 3,000 miles—from the mouth of the Mackenzie to the delta of the Mississippi—this route is uninterrupted by mountains. In fact, there is not even a ridge of hills high enough to interfere with the movements of the feathered travelers, and the greatest elevation above sea level is less than 2,000 feet. Well timbered and watered, the entire region affords ideal conditions for the support of its great hosts of migrating birds. It is followed by such vast numbers of ducks, geese. shore birds, blackbirds, sparrows, warblers, and thrushes, that observers stationed at favorable points in the Mississippi Valley during the height of migration can see a greater number of species and individuals than can be noted anywhere else in the world.

Starting in the region of Kotzebue Sound, Alaska, the route extends eastward across northern Alaska and joins another that has its origin at the mouth of the Mackenzie River. The line of flight then trends a little east of south through the great lake system of central Canada, where it is joined by two or three other routes from the northeast that have their origin on the central Arctic coast. Continuing southward the migrating flocks are constantly augmented by additions to their numbers as they pass over the great breeding grounds of central and southern Canada. Upon reaching the headwaters of the Missouri and Mississippi Rivers the route follows these streams to the Gulf coast, Arriving in this latitude many species, including the ducks and geese, the robin, the myrtle warbler, and some others spread out east and west for their winter sojourn. Others, despite the perils of a trip involving a flight of several hundred miles across the Gulf of Mexico, strike out boldly for Central America and South America. This part of the route is a broad "boulevard" extending from northwestern Florida to eastern Texas and reaching southward across the Gulf of Mexico to Yucatan and the Isthmus of Tehuantepec (fig. 17, route 4). In other words, when most of the birds (chiefly shore birds and land birds) that have come south directly through the Mississippi Valley have reached the coastal plains of Mississippi and Louisiana, they continue directly across the Gulf of Mexico. This route appears to have preference over the safer but more circuitous land or island routes by way of Texas and Florida. During the height of migration some of the islands off the coast of Louisiana are wonderful observation points for the student of birds, as the feathered travelers literally swarm over them.

Present detailed knowledge of the chief tributaries to the Mackenzie–Great Lakes–Mississippi Valley highway relates chiefly to waterfowl. Reference already has been made to the flight of the black ducks (p. 58) that reach the Mississippi Valley from southern Ontario. Some individuals of this species banded at Lake Scugog, Ontario, have been recaptured in succeeding seasons in Wisconsin and Manitoba, but the majority have been retaken at points south of the junction of the Ohio River with the Mississippi, definitely indicating their route of travel from southern Ontario.

A second route that joins the main artery on its eastern side is the one used by the blue goose, the migration route of which is probably more nearly due north and south than that of any other North American bird. The breeding grounds, which only in recent years have been discovered, are mainly in the Fox Basin region of Baffin Island and on Southampton Island. In fall these geese work southward, chiefly along the eastern shore of Hudson Bay, and upon reaching the southern extremity of James Bay they take off for what is practically a nonstop flight to the great coastal marshes of Louisiana west of the delta of the Mississippi River. In some seasons the flocks make intermediate stops among the islands and sand bars of the Mississippi, as they are

61

occasionally common in the general vicinity of Memphis, Tenn. Most of the birds push on, however, and during the period from the first of November to the last of March fully 90 percent of the species are concentrated in the area between the Sabine and the Mississippi Rivers. On the return trip northward there is sometimes a tendency for some of the blue geese to veer off toward the northwest, as they are occasionally abundant in eastern South Dakota and southeastern Manitoba. It is of particular interest to note that while some other geese and many ducks start their northward journey at the first sign of awakening spring, the blue goose remains in its winter quarters until the season there is far advanced, seemingly aware that its own breeding grounds in the Arctic are still in the grip of winter.

Great Plains–Rocky Mountain routes

A great western highway also has its origin in the Mackenzie River delta area and in Alaska. This is used chiefly by the pintail and the American widgeon or baldpate, which fly southward through eastern Alberta to western Montana. Some localities in this area, as for example, the National Bison Range at Moiese, Mont., normally furnish food in such abundance as to induce these birds to pause in their migratory movement. Upon resuming travel, some flocks move almost directly west across Idaho to the valley of the Columbia River, from which they turn abruptly south to the interior valleys of California. Others leave the Montana feeding and resting areas and turn southeastward across Wyoming and Colorado to join the flocks that are moving southward through the Great Plains (fig. 15).

Many redheads that breed in the Bear River marshes in Utah take a westerly route across Nevada to California, but some leave these breeding grounds and fly northeastward across North Dakota and Minnesota to join the flocks of these ducks that come out of the prairie regions of Canada. A few of them even travel southeastward to the Atlantic coast. This route can be traced by the records of ducks banded in summer in the Bear River marshes and retaken the following fall at points in eastern Montana, Wyoming, South Dakota, North Dakota, Minnesota, Wisconsin, Michigan, Ohio, and Maryland. Great numbers, however, follow another route from these marshes across the mountains in an easterly direction, where it almost immediately turns southward through Colorado and New Mexico, and continues to winter quarters in the Laguna Madre off the coast of Texas or in the Valley of Mexico (fig. 17, route 6). This route also represents the travels of many of the land birds of the Rocky Mountain region. Such birds perform comparatively short migrations, most of them being content to stop when they reach the middle districts of Mexico, only a few passing beyond the southern part of that country.

Observations made in the vicinity of Corpus Christi, Tex., have shown one of the short cuts (fig. 17, route 5) that is, in effect, a part of the great artery of migration. Thousands of birds pass along the coast to the northern part of the State of Vera Cruz. As the coast of the State of Tamaulipas to the north is arid and so entirely unsuited to the needs of birds that are frequenters of moist woodlands, it is probable that much or all of this part of the route is a short distance off shore. It is used by such woodland species as the golden-winged warbler, the worm-eating warbler, and the Kentucky warbler.

Pacific coast route

Although it does not present features of unusual interest, the Pacific coast route is not of so great importance as some of the others described. Because of the equable conditions that prevail, many species of birds along the coast from the Northwestern States to southeastern Alaska either do not migrate at all or else make relatively short journeys. This route has its origin chiefly in Alaska, the general region of the delta of the Yukon River marking its northern terminus, although a few species join it after a flight westward along the Alaskan Arctic coast. Some of the scoters and other sea ducks of the north Pacific region, and the diminutive cackling goose which breeds in the delta of the Yukon River, use the coastal sea route for all or most of their southward flight. The journey of the cackling goose, as shown by return records from birds banded at Hooper Bay, Alaska, has been traced southward across the Alaska Peninsula and apparently across the Gulf of Alaska to the Queen Charlotte Islands, the birds following the coast line south to near the mouth of the Columbia River. There the route swings toward the interior for a short distance before continuing south by way of the Willamette River Valley. The winter quarters of the cackling goose are chiefly in the vicinity of Tule Lake, on the Oregon-California line, and in the Sacramento Valley of California, though a few push on to the San Joaquin Valley.

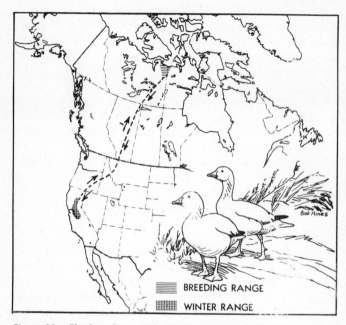

Figure 20.—The breeding range, winter range, and migration route of Ross's goose. This is the only species of which all members apparently breed in the Arctic regions, migrate south through the Mackenzie Valley, and upon reaching the United States, turn to the southwest rather than the southeast. The southern part of this route, however, is followed by some mallards, pintails, baldpates, and possibly by other ducks.

A tributary of this flyway is followed by Ross's goose which is now known to breed only in the Perry River district south of the Queen Maud Gulf on the central Arctic coast of Canada (fig. 20). Its fall migration appears to be southwest and south across the barren grounds to Great Slave and Athabaska Lakes, where it joins thousands of other waterfowl bound for their winter homes along the eastern coast of the United States and the Gulf of Mexico. But when the Ross's geese have traveled south approximately to the northern boundary of Montana, they separate from their companions, and turning to the southwest cross the Rocky Mountains and settle for the winter in California.

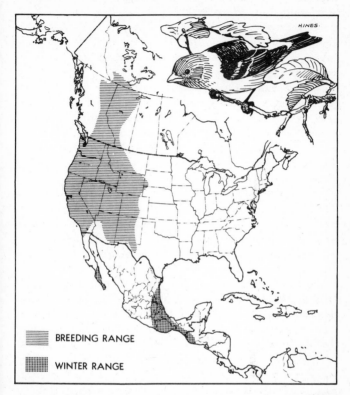

Figure 21.—Breeding and wintering ranges of the western tanager. See figure 22 for the spring route taken by the birds breeding in the northern part of the range.

The route taken by the white-winged scoters that winter on the Atlantic coast already has been indicated (p. 59). Some birds of this species, however, winter on the Pacific coast from Puget Sound south to southern California. Their passage by thousands up and down the coast has been noted as far north as northwestern British Columbia. The species is known to nest in Alaska, which may be the home of some, at least, of the scoters that winter on the Pacific coast. If such be the case, however, it must be admitted that a part of the route taken by the birds when on migration is unknown, though very few observations are available from the interior of northern British Columbia, across which the route may lie.

The southward route of those migratory land birds of the Pacific coast that in winter leave the United States extends chiefly through the interior of California to the mouth of the Colorado River and on to winter quarters in western Mexico.

The movements of the western tanager show a migration route that is in some ways remarkable. The species breeds in the mountains from the northern part of Baja California and western Texas north to northeastern British Columbia and southwestern Mackenzie. Its winter range is in two discontinuous areas—southern Baja California and eastern Mexico south to Guatemala (fig. 21). On the spring migration the birds enter the United States about April 20, appearing first in western Texas and the southern parts of New Mexico and Arizona (fig. 22). By April 30 the vanguard has advanced evenly to an approximate east-and-west line across central New Mexico, Arizona, and southern California. But by May 10 the easternmost birds have advanced only to southern Colorado, while those in the far west have reached northern Washington. Ten days later the northward advance of the species is shown as a great curve, extending northeastward from Vancouver Island to central Albert and thence southeastward to northern Colorado. Since these tanagers do not reach northern Colorado until May 20, it is evident that those present in Alberta on that date, instead of traveling northward through the Rocky Mountains, which from the location of their summer and winter homes would seem to be the natural route, reached there by the Pacific coast route to southern British Columbia and thence across the mountains, despite the fact that these are still partly covered with snow at that time.

Pacific oceanic route

The route of the Pacific golden plover is fully as interesting and as remarkable as the elliptical course followed by its eastern cousin (fig. 18). The breeding range of the eastern golden plover extends through Arctic America west to the northern coast of Alaska where, in the vicinity of Point Barrow, it meets the nesting grounds of the Pacific form, which is really an Asiatic subspecies. It breeds chiefly in the Arctic coast region of Siberia and merely overflows onto the Alaskan coast, some of the birds probably migrating south along the

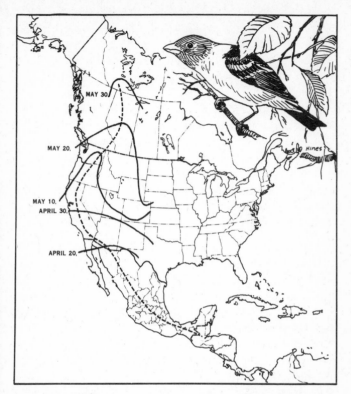

Figure 22.—Migration of the western tanager. The birds that arrive in eastern Alberta by May 20 do not travel northward along the eastern base of the Rocky Mountains, as in that region the van has then only reached northern Colorado. Instead the isochronal lines indicate that they migrate north through California, Oregon, and Washington, and then cross the mountains of British Columbia.

coast of Asia to winter quarters in Japan, China, India, Australia, New Zealand, and Oceania, including the Hawaiian Islands, the Marquesas Islands, and the Low Archipelago. Golden plovers in migration have been observed at sea on a line that apparently extends from these islands to the Aleutians, and it therefore appears certain that at least some of the Alaskan birds make a nonstop flight across a landless sea from Alaska to Hawaii. While it would seem incredible that any birds

67

could lay a course so straight as to attain these small oceanic islands, 2,000 miles south of the Aleutians, 2,000 miles west of Baja California, and nearly 4,000 miles east of Japan, the evidence admits only the conclusion that year after year this transoceanic round-trip journey between Alaska and Hawaii is made by considerable numbers of golden plovers.

The Pacific oceanic route probably is used also by the arctic terns that breed in Alaska, and possibly by those from the more western tern colonies of Canada. This species is of regular occurrence on the western coasts of both the United States and South America, indicating that the western representatives travel southward to the Antarctic winter quarters without the spectacular migration features that appear to characterize the flight of those from the eastern part of the continent (fig. 8).

Arctic routes

In the discussion of the migration of the Arctic tern (p. 38) it was noted that this species makes a very distinct west-to-east movement across northern Canada, continuing the flight eastward across the Atlantic Ocean toward the western coast of Europe. It seems likely that there are other species, including the parasitic jaeger, that regularly breed in the northern part of the Western Hemisphere but migrate back to the Old World for their winter sojourn. Some others, as the red-legged kittiwake and Ross's gull, remain near the Arctic region throughout the year, retreating southward in winter only a few hundred miles. The emperor goose in winter is found only a relatively short distance south of its breeding grounds, and eider ducks, although wintering in latitudes well south of their nesting areas, nevertheless remain farther north than do the majority of other species of ducks.

The routes followed by these birds are chiefly coastwise, and in the final analysis may be considered as being tributary either to the Atlantic or to the Pacific coast routes. The passage of gulls, ducks, the black brant, and other water birds at Point Barrow, Alaska, and at other points on the Arctic coast, has been noted by several observers, and from present knowledge it may be said that the best defined Arctic route in North America is the one that follows around the coast of Alaska.

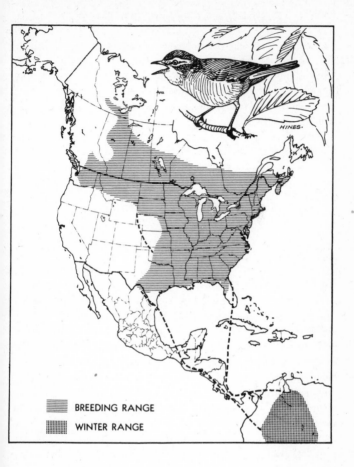

BREEDING RANGE

WINTER RANGE

Figure 23.—Distribution and migration of the red-eyed vireo. It is evident that the red-eyed vireo has only recently invaded Washington by an extension of its breeding range almost due west from the upper Missouri Valley. Like the bobolink, however (fig. 19), the western breeders do not take the short cut south or southeast from their nesting grounds, but migrate spring and fall along the route traveled in making this extension.

Evolution of Migration Routes

From the foregoing descriptions of migration routes it will be observed that the general trend of migration in most species of North American birds is northwest and southeast. It is comparatively easy to trace the probable steps in the evolution of the migrations of some species, and some routes have developed so recently that they still plainly show their origin.

The tendency is for eastern species to extend their ranges by pushing westward, particularly in the north. For example, in the Stikine River Valley of northern British Columbia and southwestern Alaska the eastern nighthawk, eastern chipping sparrow, rusty blackbird, eastern yellow warbler, redstart, and others have established breeding stations at points 20 to 100 miles from the Pacific Ocean. The robin, flicker, slate-colored junco, blackpolled and myrtle warblers, and ovenbird, all common eastern species, also are established as breeding birds in western Alaska, the ovenbird having been detected on the lower Yukon River. These birds are essentially Atlantic and Mississippi Flyway species, however, and so do not migrate in fall by any of the Pacific or Central routes, but instead retrace their journey across the mountains and move southward along the broad flyways of the East.

The red-eyed vireo, a striking example of an abundant woodland bird, is essentially an inhabitant of States east of the Great Plains, but an arm of its breeding range extends northwest to the Pacific coast in British Columbia (fig. 23). It seems evident that this is a range extension that has taken place comparatively recently by a westward movement from the upper Missouri Valley, and that the invaders retrace in spring and fall the general route by which they originally entered the country.

In the case of the bobolink, a new extension of the breeding range, and a consequent change in the migration of the species, has taken place since the settlement of the country (fig. 19). A bird of damp meadows, it was originally cut off from the Western States by the intervening arid regions. But with the advent of irrigation and the bringing of large areas under cultivation, small colonies of nesting bobolinks have appeared at various western points, and now the species is established as a regular breeder in the great mountain parks and irrigated valleys of Colorado and elsewhere almost to the Pacific coast.

70

In retracing their course to reach the western edge of the route followed by the bulk of the bobolinks that breed in the northern United States and southern Canada, these western pioneers must fly long distances along a line that runs almost due east and west.

Similarly it is possible to sketch what seems to be the logical evolution of the remarkable routes of the golden plover (fig. 18). It may be assumed that the eastern birds of this species first followed an all-land route from the South American winter quarters through Central America, Mexico, and Texas to the western parts of the Mississippi Valley. As the migration route lengthened northward with the retreat of the ice and the bird's powers of flight developed, there would be a tendency to straighten the line and to shorten it by cutting off some of the great curve through Mexico and Texas. First a short flight across the western part of the Gulf of Mexico was probably essayed. Proving successful, this was followed by flight lines that moved farther east, until finally the roundabout curve through Texas was entirely discarded and the flight made directly across the Gulf to southern Louisiana.

As the great areas in Canada were gradually added to the birds' domain, other important factors arose, the chief being the attractiveness of the vast stretches of coast and plain of the Labrador Peninsula, which in fall offered a bountiful store of berries. The fall route therefore worked eastward to the Gulf of St. Lawrence, thence southwest along the coast to Florida and across the Gulf of Mexico to the Central American mainland. A series of shortening flights followed to take out the great curve of the Atlantic coast. A relatively short ocean flight was probably attempted, say from Cape Cod to the Bahama Islands, Cuba, and Jamaica, followed eventually by the long direct oceanic route as it is now known.

As the Labrador Peninsula in spring is bound by frost and shrouded in fog while the season advances rapidly through the interior, the oceanic route proved useful only in fall, and the spring flight continued through the Mississippi Valley. This outline, although entirely hypothetical, gives a probable and fairly plausible explanation of the origin of this wonderful route, particularly when it is remembered that migration routes as now known are evolutions—age-long modifications of other routes.

The evolution of the migration route of the Pacific golden plover may be explained in a similar fashion. At first the route probably followed the Asiatic coast, through the Malay Peninsula and Oceania, thence east in a great curve to the Low Archipelago, with individuals and flocks dropping out to winter at many points along the way. The Siberian birds probably continue to follow this ancient highway, but those nesting in Alaska began a long evolutionary series of flights that cut down the length of their journey by shortening the curve, until finally the transoceanic route of the present day was developed.

This theory of the evolution of migration routes has been questioned by some ornithologists on the ground that it implies the possession in some degree of reasoning powers such as would be used by human beings. This opposition suggests that changes in migration routes might develop suddenly following mass survival of birds that were driven over the new route by a storm on some specific occasion. In the language of genetics, the new route would be, in effect, a mutation, rather than the result of an accumulation of infinitesimal variations. There is some evidence in support of this opposing theory. For example, information from the Hudson's Bay Co. post at Great Whale River, on the southeastern coast of Hudson Bay, indicates that in 1884 the snow geese suddenly changed their route from the eastern to the western coasts of Hudson and James Bays. According to one report, this change was caused by strong winds from the south which caught the birds in their fall migration and caused them to cross the entrance of James Bay from Cape Jones to the western side; the route thus reportedly forced upon them was then used in succeeding years.

Vertical Migration

In the effort to find winter quarters furnishing satisfactory living conditions, many North American birds fly hundreds of miles across land and sea. Others, however, are able to attain their objective merely by moving down the sides of a mountain. In such cases a few hundred feet of altitude correspond to hundreds of miles of latitude. Movements of this kind, known as "vertical migrations," are found wherever there are large mountain ranges. In the Rocky Mountain region they are particularly notable, as chickadees, rosy finches, juncos, pine grosbeaks, and some other species that nest in the Alpine Zone move down to the lower levels to spend the winter. It has been noted that such species as Williamson's sapsucker and the western wood pewee, which nest in the higher mountains, move down to the lower regions in August following the breeding season. There is a distinct tendency among the young of mountain-breeding birds to work down to the lower levels as soon as the nesting season is over. The sudden increases among birds in the edges of the foothills are particularly noticeable when cold spells with snow or frost occur at the higher altitudes.

Some species that normally breed in the Hudsonian or Arctic Zones find suitable breeding areas on the higher levels of the mountains, as for example the pipit, or titlark, which breeds on the tundra of Alaska and northern Canada and also south as far as Colorado on the summits of many peaks in the Rocky Mountains. On the other hand, a few species, as the Clark's crow, or nutcracker, nest at relatively low altitudes in the mountains and as the summer advances move higher up, thus performing a vertical migration that in a sense is comparable with the post-breeding movements of herons on the Atlantic coast. These illustrations show that the length of a migration route may depend upon factors other than latitude.

Vagrant Migration

The most striking feature of the migrations of some of the herons is a northward movement after the nesting season. The young of some species commonly wander late in the summer and in fall, sometimes traveling several hundred miles north of the district in which they were hatched. The little blue heron breeds commonly north to South Carolina, and by the last of July the young birds begin to appear along the Potomac, Patuxent, and Susquehanna Rivers, tributary to Chesapeake Bay. Although almost all are immature individuals, as shown by their white plumage, an occasional adult may be noted. With them come egrets and snowy herons and on occasion all three species will travel in the East as far north as New England, and in the Mississippi Valley to southeastern Kansas and Illinois. In September most of them disappear, probably returning south by the same route.

The black-crowned night heron has similar wandering habits, and young birds banded in a large colony at Barnstable, Mass., have been recaptured the same season north to Maine and Quebec and west to New York. This habit seems to be shared by some of the gulls also, although here the evidence is not so conclusive. Herring gulls banded as chicks at colonies in the Great Lakes have scattered in all directions after the breeding season, some having been recovered well north in Canada.

These movements may be considered as migration governed only by the availability of food, and they are counteracted in fall by a directive migratory impulse that carries back to their normal winter homes in the south those birds that after the nesting period attained more northern latitudes. They are not to be compared with the great invasions of certain birds from the North. Classic examples of the latter in the eastern part of the country are the periodic flights of crossbills. Sometimes these migrations will extend well south into the Carolinian Zone.

Snowy owls are noted for occasional invasions that have been correlated with the periodic maximum of Arctic foxes and the lemming cycle in the north. According to Gross (1947) 24 major invasions occurred between 1833 and 1945. The interval between these varied from 2 to 14 years, but nearly half (11) were at intervals of 4 years. A great flight occurred in the winter of 1926–27 when more than 1,000 records were received from New England alone, but the largest on record was in 1945–46 when the "Snowy Owl Committee" of the American Ornithologists' Union received reports of 13,502 birds, of which 4,443 were reported as killed. It extended over the entire width of the continent from Washington and British Columbia to the Atlantic coast and south to Nebraska, Illinois, Indiana, Pennsylvania, and Maryland. One was taken as far south as South Carolina.

In the Rocky Mountain region great flights of the beautiful Bohemian waxwing are occasionally recorded. The greatest invasion in the history of Colorado ornithology occurred in February 1917, at which time the writer estimated that at least 10,000 were within the corporate limits of the city of Denver. The last previous occurrence of the species in large numbers in that section was in 1908.

Evening grosbeaks likewise are given to performing more or less wandering journeys, and curiously enough, in addition to occasional trips south of their regular range, they travel east and west, sometimes covering long distances. For example, grosbeaks banded at Sault Ste. Marie, Mich., have been recaptured on Cape Cod, Mass., and in the following season have been retrapped at the banding station. Banding records demonstrate that this east-and-west trip across the northeastern part of the country is sometimes made also by purple finches.

Perils of Migration

The period of migration is a season full of peril for birds. Untold thousands of the smaller migrants are destroyed each year by storms and through attacks of predatory birds, mammals, and reptiles. If each pair of adult birds should succeed in raising two fledglings to maturity, the population of migratory birds would have a potential annual increase of 100 percent and the world would soon be heavily overpopulated with them. Since there is no such increase it is evident that the annual mortality from natural causes is heavy enough to keep it in check.

Storms

Of the various factors limiting the abundance of birds, particularly the smaller species, storms are the most potent. Special sufferers are those birds that in crossing broad stretches of water are forced down by a storm within reach of the waves. Such a catastrophe was once seen from the deck of a vessel in the Gulf of Mexico, 30 miles off the mouth of the Mississippi River. Great numbers of migrating birds, chiefly warblers, had accomplished nearly 95 percent of their long flight and were nearing land, when, caught by a norther against which they were unable to contend, hundreds were forced into the waters of the Gulf and drowned. On another occasion, on Lake Michigan, a severe storm came up at a time when large numbers of migratory birds were crossing and forced numerous victims into the waves. During the fall migration of 1906, when thousands of birds were crossing Lake Huron, a sudden drop in temperature accompanied by a heavy snowfall resulted in the death of incredible numbers. Literally thousands were forced into the water and subsequently cast up along the beaches, where in places their bodies were piled in windrows. On one section of the beach the dead birds were estimated at 1,000 per mile, and at another point at 5 times that number. Most of them were species that rank among our most desirable birds as destroyers of insects and weed seeds, including slate-colored juncos, tree sparrows, white-throated sparrows, swamp sparrows, winter wrens, and golden-crowned kinglets, together with many brown creepers, hermit thrushes, warblers, vireos, and others.

Of all species of North American birds, the Lapland longspur seems to be the most frequent victim of mass destruction from storms. These birds sometimes congregate in enormous numbers where grass or weed seed is abundant. Almost every winter brings in reports of their death by thousands somewhere in the Middle West. While migrating northward at night they have encountered blinding storms of wet, clinging snow, which have so bewildered them that they have flown into various obstructions, or have sunk to the ground and perished of exposure and exhaustion. In 1907 an experienced ornithologist estimated that 750,000 longspurs were lying dead on the ice of 2 lakes in Minnesota, each about 1 square mile in extent, and dead birds were reported in greater or less abundance on this occasion over an area of more than 1,500 square miles. The heaviest mortality occurred in towns, where, bewildered by the darkness and the heavy falling snow, some of the birds congregating in great numbers flew against various obstacles and were killed or stunned, while many others fell to the ground exhausted. Similar catastrophes have been reported from eastern Colorado, Nebraska, and North Dakota.

During the early part of June 1927, a hailstorm of exceptional severity in and around Denver, Colo., killed large numbers of robins, meadow larks, sparrows, and others. The lawns of parks were strewn with the bodies of these birds, and many lay dead in their nests where they were covering their eggs or young when the storm broke.

Aerial obstructions

Lighthouses, lightships, tall bridges, piers, monuments, and other aerial obstructions have been responsible for a tremendous destruction of migratory birds. Beams of the lanterns at light stations have a powerful attraction for nocturnal travelers of the air that may be likened to the fascination for lights that also is shown by many insects, particularly night-flying moths. The attraction is not so potent in clear weather, but when the atmosphere is moisture laden, as in a heavy fog, the rays have a dazzling effect that lures the birds to their death. They may fly straight up the beam and dash themselves headlong against the glass, or they may keep fluttering around the source of the light until exhausted, and then drop to the rocks or waves below. The fixed, white, stationary light located 180 feet above sea level at Ponce de Leon Inlet (formerly Mosquito Inlet), Fla., has caused great destruction of bird life even though the lens is shielded by wire netting. On one occasion an observer gathered up a bushel-basketful of warblers, sparrows, and other small passerine birds that had struck during the night. The birds apparently beat themselves to death against the wire or fell exhausted to the concrete pavement below, frequently to be destroyed there by cats or skunks. Two other lighthouses at the southern end of Florida, Sombrero Key and Fowey Rocks, have been the cause of a great number of bird tragedies, while heavy mortality has been noted also at some of the lights on the Great Lakes and on the coast of Quebec. It is the fixed white lights that cause such disasters to birds, as the stations equipped with flashing or red lights do not present such strong attractions. That it is not a mere case of geographical location has been demonstrated, for it is observed that when fixed white lights have been changed to red or flashing lights, the migrating birds are no longer endangered. At some of the light stations in England and elsewhere, shelves and perches have been placed below the lanterns to afford places where birds can rest until they have overcome their bewilderment.

For many years at the National Capital, the Washington Monument, although unilluminated, caused the destruction of large numbers of small birds, due apparently to their inability to see this obstacle in their path, towering more than 555 feet into the air. One morning in the spring of 1902 the bodies of nearly 150 warblers, sparrows, and other birds were found about its base. Then, as the illumination of the city was improved and the Monument became more visible at night, the loss became steadily less, until by 1920 only a few birds would be killed during an entire migration. On November 11, 1931, however, as part of the Armistice Day celebration, batteries of brilliant floodlights grouped on all four sides about the base of the Monument were added to the two searchlights already trained on the apex, so that the lighted shaft probably corresponds in brilliancy to a very low magnitude lighthouse lantern. Airplane pilots have ventured opinions that on a clear night it could be seen for 40 miles. It is certain that there is an extensive area of illumination, and on dark nights, when there are gusty, northerly winds and the nocturnal travelers seem to fly at lower altitudes, many of them are attracted to the Monument as to a lighthouse beacon. As they approach from the north a last-minute attempt to avoid it causes them to veer off to the east or the west where they are literally sucked in and dashed against the southern face of the shaft. During the fall migration of 1932 more than 500 warblers, vireos, thrushes, kinglets, sparrows, and others were killed. Since that year the mortality has been less, but the Monument at times remains a serious menace to birds during migration and some are killed nearly every fall.

When the torch on the Statue of Liberty in New York Harbor was kept lighted, it caused an enormous destruction of bird life, tabulations showing as many as 700 birds killed in a single month.

In September 1948, bird students were startled by news of the wholesale destruction of Maryland yellowthroats, redstarts, ovenbirds, and others that were dashed against the 1,250-foot high Empire State Building in New York City, the 491-foot high Philadelphia Saving Fund Society Building in Philadelphia, and the 450-foot high WBAL radio tower in Baltimore. In New York the birds continued to crash into the Empire State Building over a 6-hour period and their bodies were scattered over a four-block area. The mortality was so heavy in Philadelphia that it was impossible to use the sidewalk below the skyscraper until the birds had been gathered. A study of the weather conditions prevailing at this time in the Atlantic coastal region suggests the probable cause of this catastrophe. By early morning on September 11 a mass of cold, southward-flowing air had just reached New York City where it was forcing upward and was being overridden by a mass of warm, northward-flowing air. Presumably the migrants were riding the upper levels of the southbound current which, in the contact zone with the northbound current, was being deflected earthward, thus causing the birds to fly lower and lower until they were below the tower of the Empire State Building. Clouds and gusty winds in the zone of contact between the two air masses reduced visibility and disrupted avian navigation with the result that the confused travelers crashed into the stone and steel obstruction. As the cold air mass continued to move southward, the situation was repeated at Philadelphia and at Baltimore.

Exhaustion

Although it would seem that the exertion incident to the long flights of many species of migratory birds would result in their arrival at their destination in a state bordering on exhaustion, this is contrary to the truth. Both the soaring and the sailing of birds show them to be proficient in the use of factors employed in aerial transportation that only recently have become understood and imitated by aeronautical engineers. The use of ascending currents of air, employed by all soaring birds, and easily demonstrated by observing the gulls that glide hour after hour along the windward side of a ship, are now utilized by man in his operation of gliders. Moreover, the whole structure of a bird renders it the most perfect machine for extensive flight that the world has ever known. Hollow, air-filled bones, making an ideal combination of strength and lightness, and the lightest and toughest material possible for flight in the form of feathers, combine to produce a perfect flying machine. Mere consideration of a bird's economy of fuel or energy also is enlightening. The golden plover, traveling over the oceanic route, makes the entire distance of 2,400 miles from Nova Scotia to South America without stop, probably requiring about 48 hours of continuous flight. This is accomplished with the consumption of less than 2 ounces of fuel in the form of body fat. To be as economical in operation, a 1,000-pound airplane would consume in a 20-mile flight not the gallon of fuel usually required, but only a single pint.

The sora, or Carolina rail, which is such a notoriously weak flyer that at least one writer was led to infer that most of its migration was made on foot, has one of the longest migration routes of any member of the family, and easily crosses the wide reaches of the Caribbean Sea. The tiny ruby-throated hummingbird crosses the Gulf of Mexico in a single flight of more than 500 miles.

While birds that have recently arrived from a protracted flight over land or sea sometimes show evidences of being tired—as, for example, pintail ducks that have flown from the North American mainland to the Hawaiian Islands—their condition is far from being a state of exhaustion. With a few hours' rest and a crop well filled with proper food, most birds exhibit eagerness to resume their journey. The popular notion that birds find the long ocean flights excessively wearisome and that they sink exhausted when terra firma is reached, generally does not agree with the facts. The truth lies in the opposite direction, as even small land birds are so little averse to ocean voyages that they not only cross the Gulf of Mexico at its widest point, but may even pass without pause over the low, swampy coastal plain to the higher regions beyond. Under favorable conditions birds can fly when, where, and how they please. Consequently the distance covered in a single flight is governed chiefly by the food supply. Exhaustion, except as the result of unusual factors, cannot be said to be an important peril of migration.

Influence of the Weather on Migration

The state of the weather at any point has little if anything to do with the time of arrival of migratory birds. This is contrary to the belief of observers who have thought that they could foretell the appearance of various species by a study of the weather conditions. Though the insistent crescendo note of the ovenbird is ordinarily associated with the full verdure of May woods, this bird has been known to reach its breeding grounds in a snowstorm and the records of its arrival in southern Minnesota show a temperature variation from near freezing to full summer warmth. Temperatures at arrival of several other common birds vary from 14 degrees between highest and lowest temperatures to 37 degrees, the average variation being about 24 degrees.

It should be remembered that North American species spending the winter months in tropical latitudes experience no marked changes in climatic conditions from November to March or April, yet frequently they will start the northward movement in January or February. This is in obedience to physiological promptings and has no relation to the prevailing weather conditions. For migratory birds the winter season is a period of rest, a time when they have no cares other than those associated with the daily search for food or escape from their natural enemies. Their migrations, however, are a vital part of their life cycles, which have become so well adjusted that the seasons of travel correspond in general with the major seasonal changes on their breeding grounds. With the approach of spring, therefore, the reproductive impulse awakens, and each individual bird is irresistibly impelled to start the journey that ends in its summer home.

In other words, the evidence indicates that the urge to migrate is so ingrained that each species moves north in spring when the average weather that will be encountered is not unendurable. The word "average" must be emphasized since it appears obvious that the migrations of birds have so evolved that in general they synchronize with average climatic conditions. The hardy species travel early, fearless of the blasts of retreating winter, while the more delicate kinds come later when there is less danger of encountering prolonged periods of inclement weather. Some of the hardy birds pause in favorable areas and allow the spring season to advance. Then, by rapid travel they again overtake it, or, as sometimes happens, they actually outstrip it.

Occasionally this results in some hardship, and rarely in the destruction of large numbers of individuals. Cases are known where early migrating bluebirds have been overwhelmed by late winter storms. Nevertheless, unless such climatic conditions are prolonged, no serious effect on the species is noted. The soundness of the bird's instincts is evidenced by the fact that natural catastrophes, great though they may be, do not permanently diminish the avian populations.

As has been pointed out, the advance of average temperature lines, known as isotherms, is found to correspond closely with the northward movements of certain species. For example, the northward travels of the Canada goose are found to coincide with the advance of the isotherm of $35°$ F. (fig. 4).

The spring flight of migrants, if interrupted for any reason, is resumed when weather conditions again become favorable, and it is probable that all instances of arrival of birds in stormy weather can be explained on the theory that the flight was begun while the weather was auspicious. The state of the weather when a flight starts at any southern point, the relation of that place to the average position of the bird under normal weather conditions on that date, and the average rate of migratory flight, are data basic to any reasonably accurate prediction of the time arrival may be expected in northern areas.

Head winds are as unfavorable to migration as is rain or snow, as they greatly increase the labor of flight and cut down the speed of cross-country travel. If such winds have a particularly high velocity they may force down the weaker travelers, and when this happens over water areas, large numbers of birds are lost. Even strong winds that blow in the direction of aerial travel are unfavorable for the birds, as they interfere with their balance and disarrange their feathers. Moderate tail winds and cross or quartering breezes appear to offer the best conditions for the passage of the migrants.

Problems of Migration

Banding studies

The study of living birds by the banding method, whereby great numbers of individuals are marked with numbered aluminum leg rings, has come to be recognized as a most accurate means of ornithological research. Since 1920, banding work in North America has been under the direction of the Fish and Wildlife Service in cooperation with the Dominion Wildlife Service of Canada. Every year voluntary cooperators, working under permit, place bands on thousands of birds, game and nongame, large and small, migratory and nonmigratory, each band carrying a serial number and the legend, NOTIFY FISH AND WILDLIFE SERVICE, WASHINGTON, D. C., or on the smaller sizes an abbreviation thereof. When a banded bird is reported from a second locality, a definite fact relative to its movements becomes known, and a study of many cases of this nature develops more and more complete knowledge of the details of migration.

The records of banded birds are also yielding other pertinent information relative to their migrations, such as the exact dates of arrival and departure of individuals, the length of time that different birds pause on their migratory journeys to feed and rest, the relation between weather conditions and the starting times for migration, the rates of travel of individual birds, the degree of regularity with which birds return to the exact summer or winter quarters used in former years, and many other details that could be learned in no other manner. Banding stations that are operated systematically throughout the year, therefore, are supplying much information concerning the movements of migratory birds that heretofore could only be surmised. (See Appendix II, p. 92 for instructions on reporting the recovery of banded birds.)

Movements of residents

Typical migration consists of definite movements that are repeated regularly year after year, and it is to these that the term is generally restricted. It is desirable, however, if only for purposes of comparison, that some account be taken of the movements of some other birds, which, while not typical, do possess some of the characteristics of true migration. Data on this subject are being collected through bird banding.

There are several species that are customarily grouped under the heading "permanent residents," the term implying that these birds do not travel but remain throughout the year in one locality. Among these are the cardinal, the tufted titmouse, the wrentit, the Carolina wren, the house finch, the bobwhite, the California quail, and the ruffed grouse. Each species may be present constantly throughout the year, although in the northern part of the range there is probably a slight withdrawal of the breeding birds in winter. The individuals to be seen at that season, therefore, may not always be the same as those observed during the summer. It is certain, however, that these species do not regularly perform extensive journeys.

While the blue jay is disposed to be secretive, it is such a showy and noisy bird that it is not likely to escape notice. In the vicinity of Washington, D. C., as in many other places, it is present the year round, but at the end of September or early in October when the weather is becoming cooler, troops of jays are sometimes seen working southward through the trees. A corresponding northward movement occurs again in May. This is unquestionably a migration to and from some winter range, but its extent or significance is not now known. Some light is being shed on the matter, however, through the records of banded birds, and these eventually will fill in a more perfect picture of the movements of this species. One jay, banded on September 14, 1923, at Waukegan, Ill., was killed at Peruque, Mo., on November 15 of the same year; another, banded at Winnetka, Ill., on June 16, 1925, was retaken at Sulphur Rock, Ark., the following December 10; a third, banded on May 6, 1925, at Whitten, Iowa, was recaptured at Decatur, Ark., on January 22, 1926. These three birds unquestionably had made a flight that had every appearance of being a true migration to winter quarters in Missouri and Arkansas.

The black-capped chickadee is apparently resident in many places, but occasionally in winter it invades the range of the southern Carolina chickadee, and in northern Canada it is regularly a migrant.

In the coastal plain between Washington, D. C., and the Atlantic Ocean, the white-breasted nuthatch is usually absent during the summer, nesting at that season in the higher, or piedmont, country. Late in fall, however, it appears in fair abundance in the wooded bottoms, remaining at the lower levels until the following March or April.

Some birds, including the screech owl, bobwhite, Carolina wren, and mockingbird, seem to be actually sedentary, but even these are sometimes given to post-breeding wanderings. Ordinarily bobwhites that are marked with numbered bands are seldom retaken far from the area where banded, but sometimes they will travel 10 miles or more. A screech owl banded at Glenwood, Minn., in March, was recovered the following December at Emmetsburg, Iowa, 180 miles south. Such flights, however, are probably more in the nature of a search for new feeding areas, or to escape from a winged enemy, than a true migratory journey.

Migration of the white-throated sparrow

The white-throated sparrow, one of the most abundant members of its family, breeds from northern Mackenzie and the southern part of the Ungava Peninsula south to southern Montana, northern Pennsylvania, and Massachusetts. The winter range extends from the southern part of the breeding range south to the Gulf coast and northeastern Mexico. It is therefore a common migrant in many sections. Since it is a ground-feeding bird and is readily attracted to the vicinity of dwellings, it has been banded in large numbers, the total to November 14, 1949, being nearly 283,500. It would be expected that these would yield a comparable number of return records that would furnish basic data relative to the migrations of the species. Such, however, is not the case. Banded white-throated sparrows are rarely recaptured at stations between the breeding and wintering grounds. Operators of stations in the winter area, as Thomasville, Ga., and Summerville, S. C., have obtained return records showing that these birds do come back to the exact winter quarters occupied in previous seasons. The fact that they do not again visit banding stations on their migration routes indicates some unusual aspects of their travels, which it is hoped will eventually be discovered by banding studies. Problems of this type constitute definite challenges to the student of bird migration.

Migration of the yellow-billed loon

The semiannual movements of the yellow-billed loon present an unusual problem in migration. It breeds along the Arctic coast, probably from Cape Prince of Wales eastward to Franklin Bay, and also in the interior of northern Canada south to Clinton-Colden, Aylmer, and Artillery Lakes, where it is rather comon. It has been reported as already present by May 25 at the mouth of the Liard River, in southwestern Mackenzie. This coincides with the time that first arrivals are noted fully 700 miles north, at Point Barrow, Alaska. The problem has been to ascertain the route used by these birds to their principal nesting grounds in the interior.

For a long time it was believed that this big diver did not winter in large numbers anywhere on the Pacific coast, and it had been supposed that the spring route extended 2,000 miles northeastward from a wintering ground somewhere in eastern Asia to Bering Strait, then 500 miles still northeast to round Point Barrow, then 500 miles east to the coast of Mackenzie, and finally 700 miles south—in spring—to the region near the eastern end of Great Slave Lake.

The yellow-billed loon is a powerful flier, and it is probable that this suggested route is correct for those birds that breed in the northern coastal regions. A reasonable doubt may be entertained, however, whether the breeding birds of Great Slave Lake and contiguous areas reach their breeding grounds by the 700-mile flight south from the Arctic coast. Within recent years it has been found that these birds are fairly common in the maze of channels and islands off the coast of southeastern Alaska as late as the last of October and in February. Possibly they are present there during the period from November through January also, or they may at that time move farther off shore and so escape detection. If this region is an important wintering ground, as seems probable, then it is likely that the breeding birds of the interior reach their nesting grounds by a flight eastward across the mountains, a trip that is well within their flying ability, rather than by a circuitous route around the northern coast. The air-line distance from southeastern Alaska to the mouth of the Liard River is in fact less than the distance to that point from the mouth of the Mackenzie.

Differing routes to various parts of a large breeding or wintering ground, and used by large groups of individuals of other species, are not unknown. For example, the redhead duck is one of the common breeding ducks of the Bear River marshes of Utah, where a great many have been banded each summer. The recovery records of banded redheads show that while many travel westward to California, others start their fall migration in the opposite direction and, flying eastward across the Rocky Mountains, either turn southeast across the plains to the Gulf of Mexico, or deliberately proceed in a northeasterly direction to join the flocks of this species moving toward the Atlantic coast from the prairie regions of southern Canada.

Conclusions

The migration of birds as it is known today had its beginning in times so remote that its origins have been entirely obscured, and it can be interpreted now only in terms of present conditions. The causes underlying migration are exceedingly complex. The mystery that formerly cloaked the periodic travels of birds, however, has been largely dispelled through the fairly complete information that is now available concerning the extent and times of the seasonal journeys of most of the species. Many gaps, however, still remain in our knowledge of the subject. Much has been learned, and present knowledge is being placed on record, but it must be left to future study to clear away many of the uncertainties that continue to make bird migration one of the most fascinating subjects in the science of ornithology.

Each kind of bird seems to have its own reaction to its environment, so that the character of movement differs widely in the various species, and seldom do any two present the same picture. In fact, bird migration has been described as a phase of geographic distribution wherein there is a more or less regular seasonal shifting of the avian population caused by the same factors that determine the ranges of the sedentary species. If this view is correct, then it must be recognized that the far-reaching works of man in altering the natural condition of the earth's surface can so change the environment necessary for the well-being of the birds as to bring about changes in their yearly travels. The nature and extent of the changes wrought by man on the North American Continent are easily apparent. Forests have been extensively cut away and their places have been taken by second growth or cultivated land, and wide stretches of prairie and plain have been broken up, irrigated, and devoted to agriculture. These great changes are exerting a profound effect upon the native bird populations, and the various species may be either benefited or adversely affected thereby.

The Federal Government has recognized its responsibility to the migratory birds under changing conditions brought about by man, and by enabling acts for carrying out treaty obligations, it is now giving most species legal protection under regulations administered by the Fish and Wildlife Service. Much is being done by legislation for the welfare of the birds. The effectiveness of these conservation laws, however, is increased in the same measure that the people of the country become acquainted with the facts in the life histories of the migrants and interest themselves personally in the well-being of the various species. Long before the white man came to America the birds had established their seasonal lanes of migration throughout the Western Hemisphere. The economic, inspirational, and esthetic values of these migratory species dictate that they be permitted to continue their long-accustomed and still-mysterious habits of migration from clime to clime.

Appendix I—*List of Birds Mentioned in the Text*

Common name	Scientific name
American egret	*Casmerodius albus egretta*
Arctic tern	*Sterna paradisaea*
Atlantic brant	*Branta bernicla hrota*
Atlantic golden plover	*Pluvialis dominica dominica*
Bank swallow	*Riparia riparia*
Barn swallow	*Hirundo rustica erythrogaster*
Bartramian sandpiper or upland plover	*Bartramia longicauda*
Belted kingfisher	*Ceryle alcyon*
Black-and-white warbler	*Mniotilta varia*
Black-billed cuckoo	*Coccyzus erythropthalmus*
Black brant	*Branta bernicla nigricans*
Black-capped chickadee	*Parus atricapillus atricapillus*
Black-crowned night heron	*Nycticorax nycticorax hoactli*
Black duck	*Anas rubripes*
Black-headed grosbeak	*Pheucticus melanocephalus*
Blackpolled warbler	*Dendroica striata*
Black-throated blue warbler	*Dendroica caerulescens*
Bluebird	*Sialia sialis*
Blue goose	*Chen caerulescens*
Blue jay	*Cyanocitta cristata*
Bluethroat	*Cyanosylvia suecica*
Blue-winged teal	*Anas discors*
Bobolink	*Dolichonyx orizivorus*
Bobwhite	*Colinus virginianus*
Bohemian [greater] waxwing	*Bombycilla garrulus pallidiceps*
Brewer's blackbird	*Euphagus cyanocephalus*
Broad-winged hawk	*Bueto platypterus*
Bronzed grackle	*Quiscalus guiscula versicolor*
Brown [tree] creeper	*Certhia familiaris*
Cackling [Canada] goose	*Branta canadensis minima*
California quail	*Lophortyx californica*
Canada goose	*Branta canadensis*
Canvasback	*Aythya valisineria*

Cape May warbler	*Dendroica tigrina*
Cardinal	*Richmondena cardinalis*
Carolina chickadee	*Parus carolinensis*
Carolina wren	*Thryothorus ludovicianus*
Chimney swift	*Chaetura pelagica*
Chipping sparrow	*Spizella passerina*
Chuck-wills-widow	*Caprimulgus carolinensis*
Clark's nutcracker	*Nucifraga columbiana*
Cliff swallow	*Petrochelidon pyrrhonota*
Common tern	*Sterna hirundo*
Cooper's hawk	*Accipter cooperi*
Coot [American]	*Fulica americana*
Cowbird	*Molothrus ater*
Crossbill	*Loxia curvirostra*
Crow	*Corvus brachyrhynchos*
Duck hawk [peregrine falcon]	*Falco peregrinus*
Eastern fox sparrow	*Passerella iliaca iliaca*
Eider	*Somateria mollissima*
Emperor goose	*Philacte canagica*
Evening grosbeak	*Hesperiphona vespertina*
European blackbird	*Turdus merula merula*
Field sparrow	*Spizella pusilla*
Forster's tern	*Sterna forsteri*
Frigate [man-o-war] bird	*Fregata magnificens*
Golden-crowned kinglet	*Regulus satrapa*
Golden plover	*Pluvialis apricaria*
Golden-winged warbler	*Vermivora chrysoptera*
Goshawk	*Accipiter gentilis*
Grackle	*Quiscalus quiscula*
Gray-cheeked thrush	*Hylocichla minima*
Greenland wheatear	*Oenanthe oenanthe leucorhoa*
Harris's sparrow	*Zonotrichia querula*
Hermit thrush	*Hylocichla guttata*
Herring gull	*Larus argentatus*
Horned lark	*Eremophila alpestris*
Horned owl	*Bubo virginianus*
House finch	*Carpodacus mexicanus*
Ipswich sparrow	*Passerculus princeps*
Jacksnipe [see Wilson's snipe]	*Capella gallinago delicata*

Junco	*Junco hyemalis*
Kentucky warbler	*Oporonis formosus*
Kingbird	*Tyrannus tyrannus*
Knot	*Calidris canutus*
Kodiak fox sparrow	*Passerella iliaca hyperborea*
Lapland longspur	*Calcarius lapponicus*
Lapwing	*Vanellus vanellus*
Lesser yellowlegs	*Totanus flavipes*
Little blue heron	*Florida caerulea*
Loggerhead shrike	*Lanius ludovicianus*
Long-billed marsh wren	*Telmatodytes palustris*
Mallard	*Anas platyrhynchos*
Maryland yellowthroat	*Geothlypis trichas trichas*
Meadowlark	*Sturnella magna*
Migratory quail	*Coturnix coturnix*
Mockingbird	*Mimus polyglottos*
Mourning dove	*Zenaidura macroura*
Myrtle warbler	*Dendroica coronata*
Nighthawk	*Chordeilies minor*
Noddy tern	*Amous stolidus*
Northern phalarope	*Lobipes lobatus*
Northern robin	*Turdus migratorius migratorius*
Orchard oriole	*Icterus spurius*
Ovenbird	*Seiurus aurocapillus*
Pacific [American] golden plover	*Pluvialis dominica fulva*
Parasitic jaeger	*Stercorarius parasiticus*
Peregrine falcon [duck hawk]	*Falco peregrinus*
Pine Grosbeak	*Pinicola enucleator*
Pine warbler	*Dendroica pinus*
Pintail	*Anas acuta tzitzihoa*
Pipit	*Anthus spinoletta*
Poor-will	*Phalaenoptilus nuttallii*
Purple finch	*Carpodacus purpureus*
Purple martin	*Progne subis*
Purple sandpiper	*Erolia maritima*
Raven	*Corvus corax*
Red-eyed vireo	*Vireo olivaceus*
Redhead	*Aythya americana*

89

Red-legged kittiwake	*Rissa brevirostris*
Redpoll	*Acanthis flammea*
Redstart	*Setophaga ruticilla*
Red-tailed hawk	*Buteo jamaicensis*
Red-winged blackbird	*Agelaius phoeniceus*
Robin	*Turdus migratorius*
Rock wren	*Salpinctes obsoletus*
Rose-breasted grosbeak	*Pheucticus ludovicianus*
Ross's goose	*Chen rossi*
Ross's gull	*Rhodostethia rosea*
Rosy finch	*Leucosticte tephrocotis*
Rough-legged hawk	*Buteo lagopus*
Ruby-throated hummingbird	*Archilochus colubris*
Ruffed grouse	*Bonasa umbellus*
Rusty blackbird	*Euphagus carolinus*
Sanderling	*Crocethia alba*
Scarlet tanager	*Piranga olivacea*
Scaup	*Aythya marila*
Screech owl	*Otus asio*
Sharp-shinned hawk	*Accipiter striatus*
Shumagin fox sparrow	*Passerella iliaca unalaschensis*
Slate-colored junco	*Junco hyemalis*
Snow bunting	*Plectrophenax nivalis*
Snow goose	*Chen hyperborea*
Snowy heron	*Leucophoyx thula*
Snowy owl	*Nyctea scandiaca*
Song sparrow	*Melospiza melodia*
Sooty fox sparrow	*Passerella iliaca fuliginosa*
Sooty tern	*Sterna fuscata*
Sora or Carolina rail	*Porzana carolina*
Southern robin	*Turdus migratorius achrusterus*
Starling	*Sturnus vulgaris*
Swainson's hawk	*Buteo swainsoni*
Swamp sparrow	*Melospiza georgiana*
Townsend's fox sparrow	*Passerella iliaca townsendi*
Tree sparrow	*Spizella arborea*
Tufted titmouse	*Parus bicolor*
Turkey vulture	*Cathartes aura*
Turnstone	*Arenaria interpres*

Upland plover [Bartramian sandpiper]	*Bartramia longicauda*
Valdez fox sparrow	*Passerella iliaca sinuosa*
Vesper sparrow	*Pooecetes gramineus*
Western palm warbler	*Dendroica palmarum palmarum*
Western tanager	*Piranga ludoviciana*
Western wood pewee	*Contopus richardsonii*
White-breasted nuthatch	*Sitta carolinensis*
White-throated sparrow	*Zonotrichia albicollis*
White-winged scoter	*Melanitta fusca*
Widgeon	*Mareca americana*
Williamson's sapsucker	*Sphyrapicus thyroideus*
Wilson's [common] snipe	*Capella gallinago delicata*
Winter wren	*Troglodytes troglodytes*
Woodcock	*Scolopax rusticola*
Wood thrush	*Hylocichla mustelina*
Worm-eating warbler	*Helmitheros vermivorus*
Wrentit	*Chamaea fasciata*
Yakutat fox sparrow	*Passerella iliaca annectens*
Yellow-billed cuckoo	*Coccyzus americanus*
Yellow-billed loon	*Gavia adamsii*
Yellow-headed blackbird	*Xanthocephalus xanthocephalus*
Yellow palm warbler	*Dendroica palmarum hypochrysea*
Yellow warbler	*Dendroica petechia*

Appendix II—*Bird Banding*

Frequent reference has been made in this bulletin to bird banding as a means for obtaining information on the migrations and life histories of birds. Since 1920 this work in North America has been under the direction of the Fish and Wildlife Service in cooperation with the Dominion Wildlife Service of Canada. Each year birds to the number of a quarter of a million or more may be marked with numbered bands.

As anyone interested in birds, either game or nongame, may have a marked individual come into his hands, there are several pertinent details that should be remembered if the recovery record is to have maximum value in advancing the science of ornithology.

1. The reporting letter should be addressed to: Bird Banding Office, Patuxent Research Refuge, Fish and Wildlife Service, Laurel, Md.

2. In the letter print the full number of the band, including the series designation and the serial number. The series designation may be a single letter or a two- or three-digit number and may be stamped to the left or over the serial number. The series designation, if a number such as "48" or "50," is not a date and should not be so interpreted. Full numbers are correctly written as: A–678901; 48–345920; 141–543678; 20–167; 496–00517; etc.

3. If the bird is alive and uninjured, read the number carefully without removing the band, and release the bird. It may be reported again. If it is dead, remove the band and, after flattening it out, attach it to the letter with scotch tape or surgical adhesive tape. Should it be desired as a souvenir, it will be returned upon request.

4. Give in the report the exact date, the location (town, county, State, etc.) and the manner in which the bird was obtained, that is, whether it was shot, found dead, trapped, etc.

5. Print your own name and permanent address clearly on the letter.

6. Keep a record of the band number and refer to it should there be any subsequent correspondence about it with the Service. The number is always the clue to any record of a banded bird.

Some bands may bear the inscription "Notify F. and Wildlife Service, Washington, D. C." or "Notify Biological Survey, Washington, D. C.," and on the smaller sizes these may be abbreviated to "F. and W. Serv. Wash. D. C." or "Biol. Surv. Wash. D. C."

All reports of the recovery of banded birds will be acknowledged with the name of the bird, the date and place where it was banded, and the name and address of the bander.

The banding of birds is done by regular officers of the United States and Dominion Services, by biologists and technicians of the States and Provinces, and by volunteer cooperators who are specially licensed under the provisions of the Migratory Bird Treaty Act. The banding of migratory waterfowl is largely restricted to Federal and State officers and is done chiefly in refuge areas. Most nongame birds are banded by volunteer cooperators who are scattered over the United States, Canada, and Alaska. The bands are furnished without charge by the Service but each station operator supplies his own traps and other equipment.

To participate in this work, certain rules must be adhered to. Applicants for banding permits:

1. Must be at least 18 years of age.

2. Must be thoroughly competent to identify positively all local birds.

3. Must have their ability vouched for by three recognized ornithologists or by other banders.

Application blanks for the Federal permits required may be obtained from the Bird Banding Office, Patuxent Research Refuge, Fish and Wildlife Service, Laurel, Md., or, in Canada, from the Chief, Dominion Wildlife Service, Ottawa, Ontario.

Bibliography

Since almost every faunal paper on birds has a bearing on the subject of migration, only a few can be listed in this publication. Those included were selected to aid the student wishing to pursue the subject further and to cover not only all cited in the text but also others consulted and used in its preparation.

ALLARD, H. A.
    1928. Bird migration from the point of view of light and length of day changes. Am. Naturalist 62, pp. 385–408.
AUSTIN, O. L., JR.
    1928. Migration-routes of the Arctic tern (*Sterna paradisaea* Brunnich). Northeastern Bird Banding Assn. Bull., vol. 4, pp. 121–125.
BAIRD, S. F.
    1866. The distribution and migration of North American birds. Am. Jour. Sci., vol. 41, pp. 78–90, 184–192, 337–347.
BERGTOLD, W. H.
    1926. Avian gonads and migration. The Condor, vol. 28, pp. 114–120.
BISSONETTE, THOMAS HUME
    1936. Normal progressive changes in the ovary of the starling (*Sturnus vulgaris*) from December to April. The Auk, vol. 53, pp. 31–50, illus.
    1939. Sexual photoperiodicity in the blue jay (*Cyanocitta cristata.*) Wilson Bull., vol. 51, pp. 227–232, pls. 9–11.
CLARK, AUSTIN H.
    1925. Animal flight. Sci. Monthly, vol. 20, pp. 5–20.
CLARKE, W. E.
    1912. Studies in bird migration. 2 vol., illus. London.
COOKE, MAY THACHER
    1937. Flight speed of birds. U. S. Dept. Agr. Cir. 428, 13 pp.
    1945. Transoceanic recoveries of banded birds. Bird-Banding, vol. 16, No. 4, pp. 123–129.
COOKE, W. W.
    1888. Report on bird migration in the Mississippi Valley in the years 1884 and 1885. U. S. Dept. Agr., Div. Econ. Ornith. Bull. 2, 313 pp., illus.
    1904. Distribution and migration of North American warblers. U. S. Dept. Agr., Div. Biol. Survey Bull. 18, 142 pp.
    1904. The effect of altitude on bird migration. The Auk, vol. 21, pp. 338–341.
    1905a. Routes of bird migration. The Auk ,vol. 22, pp. 1–11.
    1905b. The winter ranges of the warblers (*Mniotiltidae*). The Auk, vol. 22, pp. 296–299.
    1906. Distribution and migration of North American ducks, geese, and swans. U. S. Dept. Agr., Bur. Biol. Survey Bull, 26, 90 pp.
    1908. Averaging migration dates. The Auk, vol. 25, pp. 485–486.
    1910. Distribution and migration of North American shore birds. U. S. Dept. Agr., Bur. Biol. Survey Bull. 35, 100 pp., illus.
    1913a. Distribution and migration of North American herons and their allies. U. S. Dept. Agr., Bur. Biol. Survey Bull. 45, 70 pp., illus.
    1913b. The relation of bird migration to the weather. The Auk, vol. 30, pp. 205–221, illus.
    1914. Distribution and migration of North American rails and their allies. U. S. Dept. Agr. Bull. 128, 50 pp. illus.

1915a. Bird migration.   U. S. Dept. Agr. Bull. 185, 47 pp., illus.
1915b. Bird migration in the Mackenzie Valley.   The Auk, vol. 32, pp. 442–459, illus.
1915c. Distribution and migration of North American gulls and their allies. U. S. Dept. Agr. Bull. 292, 70 pp., illus.
1915d. The yellow-billed loon: A problem in migration.   The Condor, vol. 17, pp. 213–214.

COUES, E.
1878. Birds of the Colorado Valley, a repository of scientific and popular information concerning North Amercian ornithology.   U. S. Dept. Interior Misc. Pub. 11, 807 pp., illus.

DELURY, RALPH E.
1938. Sunspot Influences.   Jour. Royal Astron. Soc. of Can., pt. 1, March 1938, pt. 2, April 1938, 50 pp.

DIXON, JOSEPH
1916. Migration of the yellow-billed loon.   The Auk, vol. 33, No. 4, pp. 370–376.

EATON, RICHARD JEFFERSON
1933–34. The migratory movements of certain colonies of herring gulls. Bird-Banding, vol. 4, No. 4, pp. 165–176; vol. 5, No. 1, pp. 1–19; vol. 5, No. 2, pp. 70–84.

FARNER, DONALD S.
1945. The return of robins to their birthplaces.   Bird-Banding, vol. 16, No. 3, pp. 81–99.

FURLONG, W. R.
1933. Land-birds in a gale at sea.   Bird Lore, vol. 35, No. 5, pp. 263–265.

GÄTKE, H.
1895. Heligoland as an ornithological observatory, the results of fifty years' experience.   (Transl. from the German by R. Rosenstock).   599 pp., illus. Edinburgh.

GORDON, DONALD A.
1948. Some considerations of bird migration: continental drift and bird migration.   Science, vol. 108, pp. 705–711.

GRIFFIN, DONALD R.
1940. Homing experiments with Leach's petrels.   The Auk, vol. 57, No. 1, pp. 61–74.
1943. Homing experiments with herring gulls and common terns.   Bird-Banding, vol. 14, No. 1 and 2, pp. 7–33.
1944. The sensory basis of bird navigation.   Quart. Rev. of Biol., vol. 19, No. 1, pp. 15–31.

GRINNELL, J.
1931. Some angles in the problem of bird migration.   The Auk, vol. 48, pp. 22–32.

GROSS, A. O.
1927. The snowy owl migration of 1926–27.   The Auk, vol. 44, pp. 479–493, illus.
1947. Cyclic invasions of the snowy owl and the migration of 1945–46.   The Auk, vol. 64, No. 4, pp. 584–601.

HARRISON, T. H.
1931. On the normal flight speeds of birds.   Brit. Birds, vol. 25, pp. 86–96.

JAEGER, EDMUND C.
1948. Does the poor-will "hibernate"?   The Condor, vol. 50, p. 45.
1949. Further observations on the hibernation of the poor-will.   The Condor, vol. 51, pp. 105–109.

Lewis, Harrison F.
  1937. Migrations of the American brant (*Branta bernicla hrota*). The Auk, vol. 54, pp. 73–95.
Lincoln, F. C.
  1917. Bohemian waxwing (*Bombycilla garrula*) in Colorado. The Auk, vol. 34, p. 341.
  1922. Trapping ducks for banding purposes: with an account of the results obtained from one waterfowl station. The Auk, vol. 39, pp. 322–334, illus.
  1924a. Banding notes on the migration of the pintail. The Condor, vol. 26, pp. 88–90.
  1924b. Returns from banded birds, 1920 to 1923. U. S. Dept. Agr. Bull. 1268, 56 pp., illus.
  1926. The migration of the cackling goose. The Condor, vol. 28, pp. 153–157, illus.
  1927a. Notes on the migration of young common terns. Northeastern Bird Banding Assoc. Bull., vol. 3, pp. 23–28, illus.
  1927b. Returns from banded birds, 1923 to 1926. U. S. Dept. Agr. Tech. Bull. No. 32, 95 pp., illus.
  1928. The migration of young North American herring gulls. The Auk, vol. 45, pp. 49–59.
  1934a. Distribution and migration of the redhead (*Nyroca americana*). Trans. 20th Am. Game Conf., pp. 280–287, map.
  1934b. The operation of homing instinct. Bird-Banding, vol. 5, No. 4, pp. 149–155.
  1935a. Ancestral highways of the sky. American Forests, vol. 41, No. 4, pp. 157, 159, and 196, 4 figs.
  1935b. The migration of North American birds. U. S. Dept. Agr. Cir. 363, 72 pp., 29 figs., bibliog.
  1935c. The waterfowl flyways of North America. U. S. Dept. Agr. Cir. 342, 12 pp., illus.
  1936. Trans-Atlantic flight of gull-billed tern. The Auk, vol. 53, No. 3, p. 331.
  1937a. The enigma of bird migration. Sci. Digest, vol. 1, No. 5, pp. 63–65.
  1937b. Our greatest travelers. In "The Book of Birds," Nat. Geog. Soc., vol. 2, pp. 301–350, 1937.
  1939a. The migration of American birds. Doubleday, Doran & Co., New York, pp. 1–xii and 1–189, col. pl. 1–xii, maps 1–22.
  1939b. The individual vs. the species in migration studies. The Auk, vol. 56, No. 3, pp. 250–254.
  1940. When the dove travels. Outdoor Georgia, vol. 1, No. 4, pp. 9 and 22 (1 map).
  1941. The waterfowl flyways. "Wild Ducks," Am. Wildlife Inst., pp. 20–29.
  1942a. La migración de aves en el Hemisferio Occidental. Pub. and dist. by Panam. Sec. of the Int. Comm. for the Protection of Birds. Pp. 1–12, illus. (maps). Both Spanish and English versions.
  1942b. Migration routes and flyways. In "Ducks, Geese and Swans of North America," by Francis H. Kortright, Am. Wildlife Inst., pp. 47–53.
  1944a. Regulation by flyways. Am. Rifleman, vol. 92, No. 11, pp. 21–23, 26, illus. (3 maps).
  1944b. Chimney swift winter range discovered. The Auk, vol. 61, No. 4, pp. 604–609, map.
  1945a. The mourning dove as a game bird. Fish and Wildlife Serv. Cir. 10, pp. 1–8, illus.
  1945b. Flyway regulations. Trans. 10th N. A. Wildlife Conf., pp. 50–51.

1946. Keeping up with the waterfowl. Audubon Mag., vol. 48, No. 3, pp. 194–205, 7 illus., 10 maps. Reprinted as Fish and Wildlife Serv. Leaflet 294, April 1947, pp. 1–10.

1949. The Mississippi flyway. Lead-off chapter in "Wildfowling in the Mississippi Flyway" ed. by Eugene V. Connett, D. Van Nostrand Co., New York, pp. 1–18, map, 12 photos.

LOWERY, GEORGE H.

1945. Trans-Gulf spring migration of birds and the coastal hiatus. Wilson Bull., vol. 57, No. 2, pp. 92–121, pls. 9, 10.

1946. Evidence of trans-Gulf migration. The Auk, vol. 63, No. 2, pp. 175–211.

MCMILLAN, NEIL T.

1938. Birds and the wind. Bird Lore, vol. 40, No. 6, 3 plates. Reprinted Smithsonian Rept. for 1939, pp. 355–363.

MAGEE, M. J.

1928. Evening grosbeak recoveries. Northeastern Bird Banding Assoc. Bull., vol. 4, pp. 56–59.

MAIN, JOHN S.

1932. The influence of temperature on migration. Wilson Bull., vol. 44, pp. 10–12.

MAY, J. B.

1929. Recoveries of black-crowned night herons banded in Massachusetts. Northeastern Bird Banding Assoc. Bull., vol. 5, pp. 7–16, illus.

PALMÉN, J. A.

1893. Report on the migration of birds. Transl. from the German by C. W. Shoemaker. Smithsonian Inst. Ann. Rept., 1892, pp. 375–396, illus.

PHILLIPS, J. C., and F. C. LINCOLN

1930. American waterfowl: their present situation and the outlook for their future. Houghton Mifflin Co., Cambridge, Mass., pp. i–xv, 1–312, illus.

POUGH, RICHARD H.

1948. Out of the night sky. Audubon Mag., vol. 50, No. 6, pp. 354–355, illus.

RENSE, WILLIAM A.

1946. Astronomy and ornithology. Popular Astron., vol. 54, No. 2, pp. 1–19.

ROBBINS, CHANDLER S.

1949. Weather and bird migration. The Wood Thrush, vol. 4, No. 4, pp. 130–144.

ROWAN, W.

1925. Relation of light to bird migration and developmental changes. Nature [London] vol. 115, pp. 494–495.

1926. On photoperiodism, reproductive periodicity, and the annual migrations of birds and certain fishes. Boston Soc. Nat. Hist. Proc., vol. 38, pp. 147–189.

1930a. Experiments in bird migration. II. Reversed migration. Nat. Acad. Sci. Proc., vol. 16, p. 520–525.

1930b. The mechanism of bird migration. Sci. Progress, vol. 25, pp. 70–78.

1931. The riddle of migration. Williams & Wilkins, Baltimore, pp. i–xiv, 1–151, illus.

SNYDER, L. L.

1943. The snowy owl migration of 1941–42. Wilson Bull. vol. 55, No. 1, pp. 8–10.

TAVERNER, P. A.

1935. Continental land masses and their effect upon bird life. The Condor, vol. 37, pp. 160–162, 2 illus.

WARNER, LUCIEN H.

1931. The present status of the problems of orientation and homing by birds. Quart. Rev. of Biol., vol. 6, No. 2, pp. 208–214.

WATSON, J. B., and K. S. LASHLEY

1915. An historical and experimental study of homing. Carnegie Inst. Washington, Dept. Marine Biol. Papers, vol. 7, pp. 1–60, illus.

WETMORE, A.

1923. Migration records from wild ducks and other birds banded in the Salt Lake Valley, Utah. U. S. Dept. Agr. Bull. 1145, 16 pp., illus.

1926. The migration of birds. Harvard Univ. Press, Cambridge, Mass., pp. I–VIII, 1–217, illus.

1932. Bird migration. Sci. Monthly, vol. 34, pp. 459–462.

WILLIAMS, GEORGE G.

1945. Do birds cross the Gulf of Mexico in Spring? The Auk, vol. 62, No. 1, pp. 98–111, map.

1947. Lowery on trans-Gulf migration. The Auk, vol. 64, No. 2, pp. 217–237.

WINKENWERDER, H. A.

1902. The migration of birds with special reference to nocturnal flight. Wisconsin Nat. Hist. Soc. vol. 2 n. s. pp. 177–263, illus.

WOLFSON, ALBERT

1940. A preliminary report on some experiments on bird migration. The Condor, vol. 42, No. 2, pp. 93–99.

1945. The role of the pituitary, fat deposition, and body weight in bird migration. The Condor, vol. 47, No. 3, pp. 95–127.

1948. Bird migration and the concept of continental drift. Science, vol. 108, No. 2793, pp. 23–30.

WOODBURY, ANGUS M.

1941. Animal migration—periodic response theory. The Auk, vol. 58, pp. 463–505.

YEAGLEY, HENRY L.

1947. A preliminary study of a physical basis of bird navigation. Jour. Applied Physics, vol. 18, No. 12, pp. 1035–1063.

Index

O